Henry Power of Halifax:

A seventeenth century Physician and Scientist

J.T. Hughes

Rimes House

Oxford

2010

Henry Power of Halifax:
A Seventeenth Century Physician and Scientist
J.T. Hughes

First published in 2010 by
Rimes House
2 Bishop Kirk Place
Oxford OX2 7HJ

British Library Cataloguing in Publication Data
A catalogue record of this book is available in the British Library

Henry Power of Halifax:
A seventeenth Century Physician and Scientist
Hughes, J.T. 1928-

1. Henry Power. 2. Biography. 3. 17th Century Science. 4. Medical History.

ISBN 978-1-874317-04-3

Typeset in Sabon and printed by
The Holywell Press Ltd
15-17 Kings Meadow
Ferry Hinksey Road
Oxford OX2 0DP

PREFACE

THIS BOOK ACCOMPANIES the edition of Henry Power's *Experimental Philosophy* published by Rimes House, Oxford, in 2009. Henry Power, an important 17th century physician and scientist, is comparatively unknown, which neglect is partly explained by his early death. *Experimental Philosophy* (London : Printed by T. Roycroft, for John Martin, and James Allestry, at the Bell in S. Pauls Church-yard, 1664) is his only publication (Fig. 1.1). Whilst copies are held by several libraries, the book is rare. A modern edition is out of print.[1] To remind historians of science of Power's work, a photographic reprint of *Experimental Philosophy* has been produced from a copy in the possession of the author.

Power, after his education at Christ's College, Cambridge, spent the whole of his life in the West Riding of Yorkshire, first at his childhood home in Halifax and later in Wakefield. His career was that of a physician and scientist. His observations in natural history and in experimental science commenced in Cambridge and continued in Halifax, which location, away from the centres of research of Oxford, Cambridge, and London, further explains his obscurity. An important friend and collaborator was Richard Towneley of Towneley Hall, near Burnley.

Power's contributions to science deserve more than a mention in the history of that subject. His experiments on air pressure preceded those of Robert Boyle (1627-1691) and his account of microscopy in *Experimental Philosophy* appeared before the publication of *Micrographia* by Robert Hooke (1635-1703). This assertion of Power's priority does not detract from the pre-eminence of Boyle and Hooke in these subjects. It does describe what was achieved by an observer and experimenter in 17th century Yorkshire, occupied with the busy clinical practice of a physician. Power was one of the first founders of the Royal Society and presented the results of his scientific experiments at their meetings.

This present account summarises what is readily known of the life of Power and his career in medicine and science. The source of this information is his book and his numerous papers, mainly preserved in the British Library. In the remote past, the *Transactions of the Halifax Antiquarian Society* carried articles on Power and three more articles have been added by the present author. Otherwise the literature on Power is sparse and widely scattered. The general histories of science do not mention Power. The two volume compilation of A. Wolf : *A History of Science, Technology and Philosophy in the 16th and 17th Centuries* (London, George Allen & Unwin Ltd, 1935, 1950, 1962), despite having run to three editions, has no mention of Power, who contributed to all three of the subjects on the title page.

REFERENCE

1   Power, H. *Experimental Philosophy*. Reprint of the 1664 edition with introduction by Marie Boas Hall. New York and London : Johnson Reprint Corporation, 1966.

To my wife, Catherine

CONTENTS

CHRONOLOGY OF THE
LIFE AND TIMES OF HENRY POWER

1578	Birth of William Harvey
1608	Birth of John Milton
1617	Matriculation at Gonville and Caius College, Cambridge of Francis Glisson
1625	Death of James I and accession of Charles I
1624	7th June. Baptism in Annesley Church, Nottinghamshire of Ellen, Power's sister
1625	12th February. Matriculation of John Milton at Christ's College, Cambridge
1626	Birth of Power in Annesley. No record found.
1628	Publication of William Harvey's *De Motu Cordis*
	Birth of John Bunyan
1631	Death of John Donne
1632	Birth of Prince Charles, *later* Charles II
	Birth of Christopher Wren, John Locke, and Baruch Spinoza
	26th April. Matriculation at Christ's College of Thomas Wilding, tutor to Power
1636	Appointment of Francis Glisson as Regius Professor of Physic, Cambridge University
1638	Publication of Milton's *Lycidas*
1639	First Bishops' War
1641	9th June. Matriculation of Power as a pensioner of Christ's College
1642	Death of Galilleo. Birth of Isaac Newton
	Publication of Thomas Browne's *Religio Medici*
1645	Power graduates BA at Cambridge
1646	Publication of the first edition of Browne's *Pseudodoxia Epidemica*
	Abolition of the Episcopacy
1647	Parliamentary Army occupies London
1648	Power graduates MA at Cambridge
	Peace of Westphalia ends the Thirty Years War
1649	Execution of Charles I. Abolition of the monarchy and the House of Lords
	Interregnum 1649-1660 begins
1651	Publication of Thomas Hobbes' *Leviathan*
1653	6th May, Power conducts his barometric experiments on Halifax Hill
1654	Publication of Francis Glisson's *Anatomia Hepatis*
1655	Power marries Margery Foxcroft in Halifax
	Power gains his Cambridge MD

1657	Death of William Harvey
1658	Death of Oliver Cromwell
1659	Richard Cromwell abdicates. End of the Protectorate. Power becomes the legal owner of New Hall, Elland. He and his wife, Margery, take up residence.
1660	Restoration of Charles II
1661	The Cavalier Parliament (to 1679)
1662	Death of Pascal
1663	Foundation of the Royal Society. Power proposed in May and elected a Fellow on 1st July.
1664	Publication of *Experimental Philosophy*
1664	7th October. Removal of Power to Wakefield
1665	Outbreak of the Great Plague. Wakefield has many cases.
1666	The Great Fire of London
1667	Publication of Thomas Spratt's *History of the Royal Society*
1668	Death of Power in Wakefield. Buried 23rd December in All Saints, Wakefield Parish Church, now Wakefield Cathedral.
1669	Power's Will, proved by his widow, Margery, on 2nd June.
1700	Death of Power's only son, George, buried 10th May at Elland, Halifax.

ACKNOWLEDGEMENTS

I AM INDEBTED for help in this work to many persons and institutions. The primary source of information on Henry Power are the voluminous papers held in the British Library and I am deeply grateful for being allowed access to these in the comfortable surroundings of their manuscript room. Several documents have been reproduced in this work and I acknowledge and thank the British Library for their expert photography and permission to publish. The British Library, of which I am a Friend, is one of our great national assets. For many years I have spent part of most weekdays in the Bodleian library, where I have consulted scores of books relating to Power as well as accounts concerned with his home in Halifax and his education in Cambridge. Having used the Bodleian Library for over 50 years, I have met several of Bodley's librarians but I mention especially the help and friendship of David Vaisey, whose tenure of office coincided with my work on Power. Elsewhere in Oxford, I have read in the libraries of the Colleges of All Souls, Christ Church, Queens, Magdalen and St Johns and I thank their librarians for this access. The librarian of the Oxford History of Science Museum, G.T. Wright, MA, was especially helpful for access to and advice on books and journals relating to the history of the telescope and microscope.

In Halifax I have read extensively in the Central Halifax Library, whose books and journals on Halifax are conveniently accessible. The reproductions of the lithographs of views of Halifax by John Horner were all provided by Sara Darling, Principal Librarian of the Central Halifax Library. Elsewhere in Yorkshire, I thank Mrs D. Scriven, Archivist in Wakefield, for providing the burial record of Power in All Saints, Wakefield Parish Church. Sara Slinn of the Borthwick Institute of Historical Research in York answered my queries on Power's education. I thank Adrian Henstock, Principal Archivist in Nottingham, for his examination of the Register of Baptisms for Annesley, 1624-1633 (PR 2826).

In Cambridge I have much indebtedness to acknowledge, and especially for their cordial welcome to an Oxford academic to use their libraries and records. Prof. Geoffrey Martin, Archivist and Keeper of the Muniment Room of Christ's College provided the record in their Admissions Book of Power's entry into the College, most valuable evidence of his place of birth, Annesley, and his schooling in Halifax under a Mr Higginson. This record of his age (15) is the most reliable evidence for the year of his birth. The Cambridge University Library has been invaluable in providing access to the University Archives through the help of Jacqueline Cox. The Staff of the National Monument Record Centre in Swindon provided photographs of New Hall, Elland, Halifax and of Towneley Hall, Lancashire.

Every biographer refers to previous work on his subject and I have given references at the end of each chapter and in the bibliography. There are two authors who deserve particular mention. J.W. Clay of Halifax made a detailed study of most of the records of Power, and his findings were presented in 1917 to the Halifax Antiquarian Society and published in their *Transactions*. My other academic benefactor is Charles Webster, a great friend, whose research on Henry Power's experiments with mercury has never been bettered.

In Oxford, an academic benefits from membership of a college and I am grateful for a fellowship of Green College and its successor Green Templeton College. My final thanks are to my wife, Catherine, for her support throughout all the research and writing of this work, including reading all drafts with the expert eye of an historian.

Green Templeton College
University of Oxford,
Woodstock Road
Oxford OX2 6HG

LIST OF ILLUSTRATIONS

Chapter 1

Introduction

Henry Power occupies an important place in the science and medicine of the 17th century, the century in which the gains in knowledge made in the 16th century were extended and consolidated. These discoveries of the 16th century embraced many fields. The exploration of the world by the Europeans beyond that known in their immediate vicinity had a modest beginning in the 15th century by the Portuguese sailors in their caravels and by Columbus, from Italy, but sailing from Spain. By land and sea, exploration continued apace in the 16th century. In the 17th century, the Europeans began to colonise the discovered new worlds. By the middle of the 16th century, Europe was experiencing the Renaissance, the progress of which varied in different countries. There were important changes in literature, art and music, but here we are concerned with science and medicine, in which subjects the greatest advances were in the cities of what is now Italy. There was also progress in France, Switzerland, Germany, and the Low Countries. In all these countries, the Thirty Years War from 1618-1648 was a major disruption. Progress in the arts and sciences in the Renaissance depended on the control exercised by the Church and important was the challenge to the established Church by reformers such as Martin Luther and John Calvin. Acceptance of new theories in science depended on the relaxation of current religious dogma. For many centuries the Church had preserved its beliefs and doctrines, and not only on matters that today we would confine to religion. For centuries any observation or theory concerning the celestial, physical or natural world had to conform to the accounts in the scriptures. The Church had also embraced the teaching of Aristotle, whose pronouncements were accorded an authority similar to that given to scriptural texts. In tracing the development of European medicine and science, the schools of Montpellier, Padua, and Leiden – three of the most famous in the 17th century – are illustrative. In this century, the fame of Montpellier was waning, that of Padua achieved its greatest lustre, whilst youthful Leiden was to surpass both in achievement. Paris also commanded respect in 17th century medicine.

Power never studied abroad and travelled infrequently after his education at Cambridge. His education continued independently, assisted by correspondence with Dr Thomas Browne and his acquisition of an extensive library modelled on that of Browne.[1] Power was familiar with the notable physicians and scientists of Europe and possessed many of their textbooks. He was an early scientist and his contributions are important in the development of science in

England. The science of Sir Thomas Browne is evident in the numerous editions of his *Vulgar Errors*, which book, in his lifetime, brought him fame throughout Europe, although his views on science were primitive and naïve.[2] Power, in some measure a pupil of Browne, is a more convincing scientist. The reputations of Robert Boyle and Robert Hooke are greater and deservedly so, yet Power has prior claims. It is a modern concept that the date of publication of scientific discoveries establishes the priority of the researcher and today scientific journals provide this opportunity. In the case of Power his only book, *Experimental Philosophy* (Fig. 1.1), establishes the priority of some of his discoveries but his manuscripts also indicate that some of his experiments predated those of other scientists.

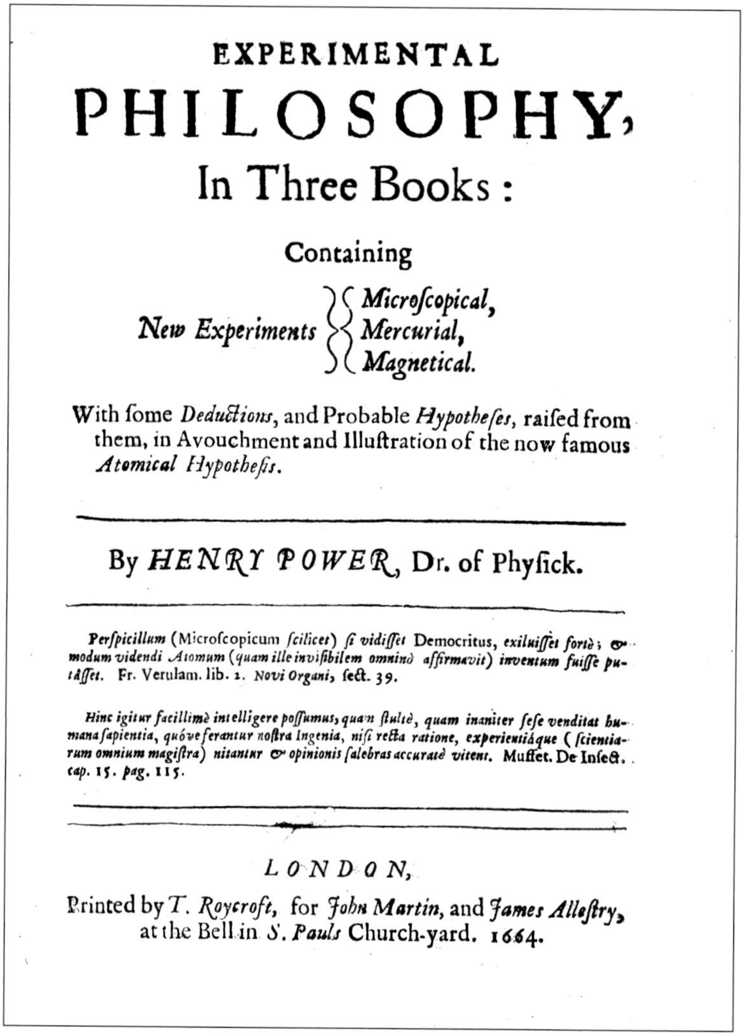

EXPERIMENTAL

PHILOSOPHY,

In Three Books :

Containing

New Experiments ⟩⟨ Microscopical, Mercurial, Magnetical.

With some *Deductions*, and Probable *Hypotheses*, raised from them, in Avouchment and Illustration of the now famous *Atomical Hypothesis*.

By *HENRY POWER*, Dr. of Physick.

Perspicillum (Microscopicum *scilicet*) *si vidisset* Democritus, *exiluisset forsè*; & *modum videndi Atomum* (*quam ille invisibilem omninò affirmavit*) *inventum fuisse putdisset.* Fr. Verulam. lib. 1. *Novi Organi*, sect. 39.

Hinc igitur facillimè intelligere possumus, quam stultè, quam inaniter sese venditat humana sapientia, quóve ferantur nostra Ingenia, nisi rectà ratione, experientiáque (scientiarum omnium magistra) nitantur & opinionis falebras accuratè vitent. Muffet. De Insect. *cap. 15. pag. 115.*

LONDON,

Printed by *T. Roycroft*, for *John Martin*, and *James Allestry*, at the Bell in *S. Pauls* Church-yard. 1664.

Figure 1.1 Title page of Power's *Experimental Philosophy*, 1664.
The date is given as 1663.

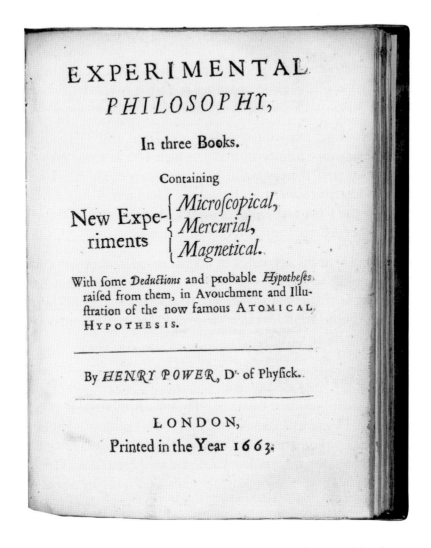

EXPERIMENTAL
PHILOSOPHY,

In three Books.

Containing

New Expe- { Microfcopical,
{ Mercurial,
riments { Magnetical.

With fome *Deductions* and probable *Hypothefes,*
raifed from them, in Avouchment and Illu-
ftration of the now famous ATOMICAL
HYPOTHESIS.

By *HENRY POWER,* Dʳ of Phyfick.

LONDON,
Printed in the Year 1663.

Figure 1.2 Title page preceeding *Liber Secundus.*, the second book,
describing the Mercurial Experiments. Note the publication date of 1663.

The work on air pressure appears in Book 2 and the title page of this second book is dated 1663 (Fig. 1.2). Power's own copy, now in the British Library, is dated 1663 in his own handwriting. And there is an intriguing 'lost book' by Henry Power. White Kennet in *Register and Chronicle* (1728), p. 541, records a book by Power, published in September 1661. As the size (octavo) of the book is stated it seems likely that some copies were printed but none appears to have survived. We know the content of this 'lost book' from Power's manuscripts as, with some minor revisions, it appears as Book 2 of *Experimental Philosophy* (1663).

Robert Hooke is rightly credited with a substantial contribution to the science of microscopy in England, and his *Micrographia* was published in 1665.[3] But the first part of *Experimental Philosophy* consists of 83 pages describing the microscopical appearances of the animal, vegetable, and mineral worlds. Power generously welcomes other scientists to this world of microscopy, concluding his work with :

> These are the few Experiments that my Time and Glass hath as yet afforded me an opportunity to make, which I hasten out into the World to stay the longing thereof ; But you may expect shortly from Doctor *Wren* and Master *Hooke*, two Ingenious Members of the Royal Society at *Gresham*, the Cuts and Pictures drawn at large, and to the very life of these and other Microscopical Representations.

Power was aware that his drawings of his microscopical observations fell short of what Wren might have achieved and he also recognised that Robert Hooke was pre-eminent in advancing the science of microscopy. But Power's book was the first English publication on microscopy and his experiments on air pressure were made before those of Boyle.

NOTES AND REFERENCES

[1]   For Power's correspondence with Sir Thomas Browne see : Keynes, G. *The Works of Sir Thomas Browne*, volumes 1-6. London : Faber and Gwyer (becoming Faber and Faber), 1928-1931, 6, pp. 275-295.

[2]   Browne. T. *Pseudodoxia Epidemica*. London : Printed for T.H. by Edward Dod, 1646. There were subsequent English editions by various publishers in 1650, 1658 (2), 1659, 1669, 1672, and 1686 and several translated into other languages.

[3]   Hooke, R. *Micrographia : or some Physiological Descriptions of Minute Bodies made by magnifying Glasses*. London : J. Allestry, 1665.

Chapter 2

Ancestors, Birth, and Childhood

The Power family bore arms in the reign of Henry VIII, when Francis Power married a daughter of the Bosseville family of New Hall.[1] This alliance began the association of the Power family with New Hall, built by the Saville family in the fifteenth century.[2] Of their three sons, we are concerned with William, whose son, another William, was Rector of Barwick in Elmet, West Riding from 1569-1594. His son – yet another William – became the Lady Margaret Preacher at Cambridge. It was the custom of the family to send the first son to Cambridge, usually to Christ's College, where, after a classical education, he would study divinity and take holy orders. After probation as a curate, a living would be found, usually in Yorkshire and often connected with some branch of the family. The living might be in the gift of Cambridge and sometimes held by Christ's College, who would favour a member of the College.

Power's Family

Henry Power's father – John Power – was not the eldest son and did not proceed to Cambridge but opted for trade, which was less prestigious, but financially more rewarding. He traded with the Continent of Europe and, unusually, sometimes with Spain, which led to his being referred to as 'the Spanish Merchant'. Trading with Spain was hazardous and often prohibited, since England and Spain were frequently on bad terms and sometimes at war. John Power was the youngest of the four sons of William Power, who also had two daughters. One daughter – Ann – married the Reverend John Favour, Vicar of Halifax. This connection brought John Power to live near his sister in Halifax. He prospered in trade and became a large property owner in Halifax. John Power married Jane, daughter of a Mr Jennings, possibly from Erdington, near Birmingham. They had a daughter, Ellen and four sons, our subject, Henry, then John, Thomas, and William. Following the family custom, our Henry – the eldest son – was destined for Cambridge. John remained in Halifax whilst Ellen, Thomas and William migrated to London. Thomas became a stationer, William a haberdasher, whilst Ellen married a William Howson.[3]

Birth at Annesley

By chance, Henry was born, not in Yorkshire, but in Nottinghamshire. John Power, his father, had a connection with Nottinghamshire and once lived in Arnold, Notts.[4] At the time of the birth of Ellen and Henry, the parents lived in Annesley, Notts. John Power had business with the family of Sir George (later

5

Figure 2.1 The South East prospect of Annesley House, as seen from the Park Gate, Nottingham Road, engraved by Richard Hall. In R. Thoroton. *The Antiquities of Nottinghamshire*, Nottingham, 1677. The picture faces p. 252.

Viscount) Chaworth, whose country seat was Chaworth Hall.[5] [6] Richard Hall engraved a picture of Annesley Hall (Fig. 2.1), which shows a fine country house with a small village and a church. This picture appears in a 1677 publication on Nottinghamshire.[7] The old Annesley Church is now a ruin and the village is much altered. Coal was discovered and the area became a colliery for the smelting of lead and iron.[8] The population expanded into a large colliery village and, in 1874, a new church, All Saints, replaced the old church.

The register of baptisms for the old Annesley Church has the record: 'Ellen Power daughter of John Power gent, baptised 7 June 1624'. It is unfortunate that no baptismal record for Henry has been found and the date of his birth must be sought elsewhere. The Register of Christ's College, Cambridge gives his age on 9 June 1641 as fifteen years, making the year of his birth as 1626. His birthplace is stated as Annesley, Notts.[9] [10] There is a rival date of his birth of 1623, which has been calculated from his memorial plaque in Wakefield Parish

Church, which records his death in 1668 at the age of forty-five years. This birth date, which was given in the old *Dictionary of National Biography*, would place Henry one year younger than his sister, Ellen. Whilst we cannot be certain, his age on entry into Cambridge is more likely to be correct than that on his memorial plaque. He was probably born in 1626.

Schooldays

The family moved to Halifax (Figs. 2.2 & 2.3), possibly about 1633, which is the date that their father purchased the Mulcture Hall. John Power had become a prominent and wealthy citizen of Halifax. Which school Henry attended is uncertain. Cambridge records state: 'Halifax under Higginson', but the accounts of the Heath Grammar School at Woodhouse, Halifax, do not mention Power or Higginson. Possibly Higginson was a private tutor, but where he himself was educated can only be conjectured as his name does not appear in the records of Oxford or Cambridge at the relevant period. Hipperholm School had not yet been founded.[11] Some Halifax boys boarded at York but their archives do not record Power or Higginson.[12]

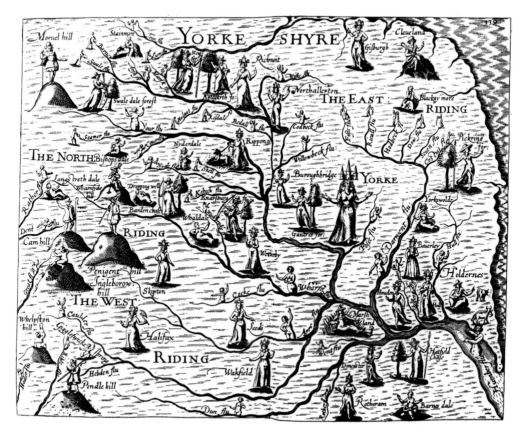

Figure 2.2 Map of Yorkshire from *Poly-albion* by Michael Drayton, 1662.

Figure 2.3 View of Halifax in an 18th century engraving.

There is little information on Power's childhood but one detail that has survived was important in deciding his career. As a child, Henry encountered Dr Thomas Browne (later Sir Thomas Browne), the author of *Religio Medici* and other literary masterpieces. Browne resided in Halifax in the years intervening between his medical education abroad and commencing his practice as a physician in Norwich. Browne had gained his Doctorate of Medicine at Leiden, but required an Oxford medical doctorate to practise as a physician, which degree could only be conferred after an interval of some years after his first Oxford degree. During this time he could not practise medicine in London, Oxford or Cambridge or elsewhere, where the medical establishment controlled medical practice. Halifax was sufficiently remote for his purpose and Browne remained there for about two years. His stay in Halifax is important in literary circles as the place where he wrote (or finished) *Religio Medici*, his first literary work. Browne was directed to Halifax because he had met and become on good terms with John Power, probably when Browne was studying medicine at Montpellier. Although the actual house in which Browne lived is uncertain it was situated in Shibden Dale, near Halifax.[13] Browne may have been a tenant of John Power to whom, it has been stated, *Religio Medicio* was dedicated.[14] What is certain is that Henry Power was directed to a career in medicine by his prolonged acquaintance with Browne. They remained good friends during Power's career and the relationship was that of a tutor to a pupil, although

Figure 2.4 North view of Heath Grammar School by John Horner. It is possible that Henry Power attended this school but the registers are incomplete.

Browne was educated at Oxford and the Continent, whilst Power proceeded only to Cambridge. In the first half of the17th century, medicine was not the prominent profession it has subsequently become. The standing of physicians was low compared with that of churchmen and lawyers and Henry was the first member of the Power family to practise medicine. As we shall describe, he was drawn to a career not only in medicine but also in the new subject of science. There was little science in England in the beginning of the 17th century but, towards the end of the century, science was well advanced, an advance in which progress Power played a prominent part.

NOTES AND REFERENCES

1 Thoresby, R. *Ducatus Leodinensis or the Topography of the Ancient and Populous Town and Parish of Leedes*, London : Maurice Atkins, 1715, p. 258.
2 Giles, C. 'New Hall, Elland; The Story of a Pennine Gentry House from circa 1490 to the mid-19th Century'. In *Old West Riding*, Oldgate, Huddersfield : 1981, edited by G. Redmonds. Vol. 1. No. 2.
3 Clay, J.W. 'Dr Henry Power of New Hall, F.R.S.,' *Transactions of the Halifax Antiquarian Society* (henceforth *THAS*), Halifax, no volume number, (1917), pp. 1-31.

[4] A deed of 1633 describes John Power as late of Arnold, Nottinghamshie, and now of Halifax. In Hanson, J.W. 'The Multure Hall', *THAS*, (1935), pp. 1-19.

[5] I am indebted to Adrian Henstock, Archivist of Nottingham, for information about Annesley.

[6] Throsby, J. Enlarged edition of Thoroton's *The Antiquities of Nottinghamshire* in 3 volumes. Nottingham : Burbage, Tupman, Wilson & Gray, 1790-1796. Republished with an introduction by M.W. Barley & K.S.S. Train, Wakefield : E.P. Publishing, 1972, 2, pp. 170.

[7] Thoroton, R. *The Antiquities of Nottinghamshire*, London : Printed by Robert White for Henry Mortlock, 1677. The picture of Annesley House faces p. 252.

[8] *The Victorian History of the County of Nottinghamshire.* Volume 2 edited by William Page. London : University of London Institute of Historical Research. Reprint of the 1910 edition, Folkstone and London : Dawsons, 1970, p. 330.

[9] In Peile, J. *Biographical Register of Christ's College.* 2 vols. Cambridge : Cambridge University Press, vol. 1, p. 477.

[10] Venn, J. and Venn, J.A. *Alumni Cantabridgienses.* Cambridge : Cambridge University Press, 1924, part 1, vol. 3, p. 389.

[11] Hughes, J.T. 'Laurence Sterne (1713-1768) and Hipperholme Grammar School, Halifax.' *Transactions of the Halifax Antiquarian Society*, 9, (2001), pp. 53-62.

[12] Stead, J. 'Dr Henry Power and his alterations at New Hall, Elland 1655-1664, in *Old West Riding*, vol. 8, no. 2, edited by J. Stead (Oldgate, Huddersfield, 1988), pp. 8-17. Stead states that Power was educated in York.

[13] Hughes, J.T. 'Sir Thomas Browne, Shibden Dale, and the writing of *Religio Medici.*' *Yorkshire History Quarterly*, 5, (2000), pp. 89-94.

[14] Webster, C. 'Henry Power's Experimental Philosophy', *Ambix*, 14, (1967), pp. 150-178. See note 6 on p. 151, which quotes Huntley, F.L. *Sir Thomas Browne,* (Ann Arbor, 1962), pp. 92-110.

Chapter 3

Education at Cambridge

For some fourteen years, Power was taught or supervised by members of the University of Cambridge.[1] The University experienced many changes in the 17th century, as did England and Scotland, when the reign of the Stuart kings succeeded that of Queen Elizabeth. The forms of religious observance in England and Scotland were divisive. Many families remained Roman Catholic, whilst a protesting religious faction was developing. King James and his successor, Charles, strove to establish a distinctive form of religion in England, with a new translation of the Bible and a new Prayer Book. Introducing these changes into Scotland, recently united with England but with a totally different culture, became a source of tension. The high churchmanship urged by Archbishop Laud was insufficient to please the Catholics and provoked a vigorous countervailing movement by the Protestants. Religious and civic affairs were now affected by the growing importance of Parliament, which, under the Tudors, had been subservient to the Sovereign. The disagreements between King and Parliament survived the reign of James I, but exploded under Charles I into the Civil Wars (1642-1646 and 1648), the execution of the King (January 1649), and the creation of the Protectorate. These disturbing national affairs were the background to Henry Power's studies at Cambridge. In the Civil Wars, Cambridge, mainly Protestant, supported the Parliament.

Foreign affairs in this period depended on relations between England (and to some extent Scotland) and Continental Europe, which in the 17th century was disturbed by the Thirty Years War (1618-1648). England was sometimes supportive of France and was usually against the interests of Spain. Alliances were made and often confirmed by royal marriages. James I had a bride from Denmark, whilst Charles I married a French princess. In the academic world, of which Cambridge was an important centre, the changes of the Renaissance, beginning in the cities of Italy, but spreading into France and other countries, affected teaching and study, particularly of the sciences. New beliefs challenged the old and the dominance of the Church was being eroded. In spite of the difficulties of wars, academic channels of information remained open, and interchange of the fruits of research continued. Cambridge, possibly more than Oxford, was in communication with similar centres of learning on the Continent of Europe.

University of Cambridge [2 3 4 5 6 7 8 9 10 11]

In the early years of the 17th century, Cambridge had little or no distinction other than as a place pursuing academic studies (Fig. 3.1). The Colleges were buildings of great beauty and architectural merit and there were tranquil river walks by the Cam and the Granta. However, the town was surrounded by largely undrained swamps, and its agriculture and animal husbandry were primitive. It was also unhealthy. Enteric disease was common and, arising from the persistent swamps, malaria was endemic. Smallpox was prevalent and there were frequent epidemics of plague. The population ranged between eight and nine thousand, of which members of the University numbered some three thousand. There was a distinct division between town and gown. The Town was governed by a Mayor, Aldermen and a Common Council and sent two members to Parliament. The University was regulated by its Statutes and was administered by the Chancellor, High Steward, Vice-Chancellor and the two Proctors. The University also sent two members directly to Parliament. In contrast to Oxford, religion tended towards Puritanism. Of those who sought a new life in North America free of religious intolerance, many had been educated at Cambridge. John Harvard, founder of Harvard University, had been at Emmanuel College.

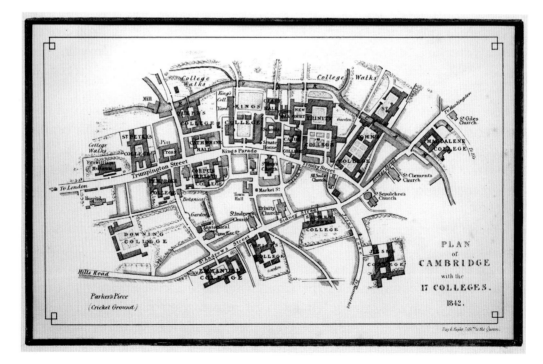

Figure 3.1 Plan of Cambridge dated 1842. Christ's College faces St Andrew's Church and is adjacent to Emmanuel College.

There were sixteen colleges, of which the two smallest in numbers of members – Catherine and Trinity – were called Halls. As now, Trinity College and St John's College were the largest. Christ's – Power's college – was third, followed by Emmanuel and Queen's. Christ's had a master, 13 fellows and 55 scholars. Other students made up the numbers to over 250 members. The scholars were of the foundation and were – or meant to be – poor students of academic promise. The other students were designated as fellow-commoners (sometimes called greater pensioners), pensioners (correctly lesser pensioners), and sizars. The distinction was partly of rank but mainly financial. There were few fellow-commoners, who were the sons of noble or wealthy families. Their larger fees obtained privileges. On occasions, they might have (or have purchased) the sole occupancy of a college room, and they dined in hall on the high table with the fellows. The sizars were the poorer students and paid lesser fees. They received the same academic tuition but were otherwise treated as of lower rank. Their accommodation was inferior and they might be lodged outside the College, wherever their parents could find and afford. Sometimes a sizar would be remunerated for serving one of the fellows. The pensioners formed the majority of students and were usually sons of clergymen or small landowners.

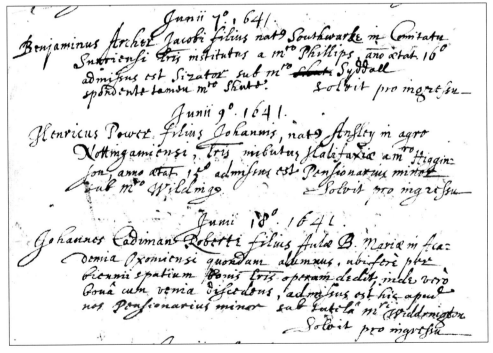

Figure 3.2 Entry of Henry Power (at age 15) in the College Admission Book. The date is June 9th, 1641. His birth is given at Annesley, Nottinghamshire and his schooling in Halifax under a Mr Higginson.

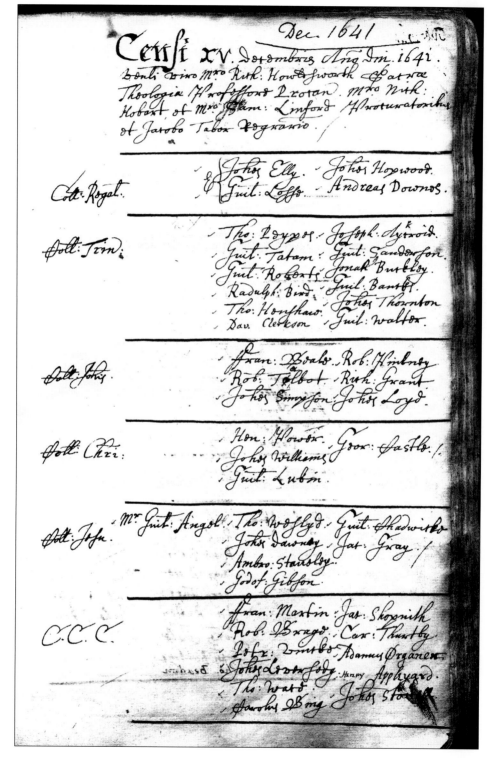

Figure 3.3 The Cambridge University record in December 1641 of Power's matriculation.

Henry Power entered Cambridge at the age of fifteen and his entry in the College Admissions Book on June 9th, 1641, is reproduced in Figure 3.2. In December, 1641, he matriculated – by a separate ceremony – into the University (Fig. 3.3). Power was admitted to his college as a pensioner under the care of a Mr Wilding. Thomas Wilding was from Selattyn in Shropshire and came to Christ's in 1632 also as a pensioner and had been a fellow since 1638. He was to be ejected in 1644 but recovered his fortunes after the Restoration and eventually succeeded his father as Rector of Selattyn. Wilding's other students, admitted in 1641 as pensioners, were William Hunt from Dowlish-Wake, Somerset, and Robert Jones from Denbighshire and Shrewsbury School. In the calendar year[12] of 1661 some 31 students were admitted to Christ's. Of these, James Wilson, Nicholas Laurence, Cuthbert Morley, Benjamin Norcliffe, and Thomas Frankland were all at school in York and might have been known to Power.[13] Nicholas Laurence was admitted as a sizar under William Power, the uncle of our Henry. John Consett was born in York and may have been to school there but arrived in Cambridge with a Master of Arts from King's College, Aberdeen. Cambridge and Christ's College were always the choice of the Power family, and Henry's uncle, William Power, was a Fellow of the College and the Lady Margaret Preacher. He led a group inclined to high churchmanship called the 'Poweritans' and was to be ejected from the College and University during the Protectorate.

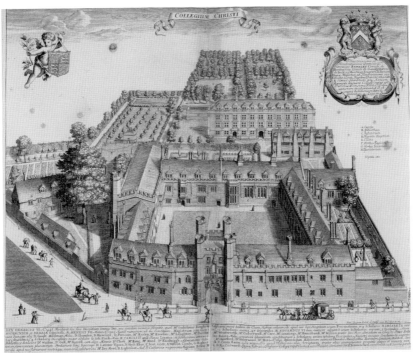

Figure 3.4 17th century engraving of Christ's College by David Loggan (1635-1692).

The splendid architecture of Christ's is evident in the 17th century engraving (Fig. 3.4) by David Loggan (1634-1692).[14] The great entrance and the front, as seen in 1809 (Fig. 3.5), is illustrated from an engraving based on a drawing by R.D. Harradon. Entering the quadrangle, the chapel is on the left and facing you on the right is the dining hall. There were several formal gardens and a bowling green. Where Power resided can only be conjectured but, if in college, he would have shared a room, known as a chamber. Even fellows sometimes shared a room and four undergraduates might be accommodated in one room.

The rules of the colleges and the university were framed to control the activities of undergraduates who might be as young as twelve years old. Encouraging or enforcing study, and preventing idleness, was achieved principally by confining the students within the College. They were only allowed into town if accompanied by their tutor or a senior person such as a master of arts. They were supposed to converse only in Latin, Greek or Hebrew – an impossible regulation to enforce. In the town they were forbidden to visit taverns or to witness boxing matches, bull fighting or cock fighting. They were prohibited from keeping dogs, falcons, hawks, and ferrets. They were not to bathe in the Cam. These prohibitions are mentioned so often as to suggest their frequent evasion by the undergraduates. The Dolphin, Rose and Mitre taverns were popular and not only entered by the townsfolk.

Figure 3.5 Entrance of Christ's College on St Andrews Street, as seen in 1809.
Engraving based on a drawing by R. D. Harradon.

University terms were as stated in the Statutes of Elizabeth I. The academic year began on the 10th of October as the Michaelmas Term, which ended on the 16th of December with the Christmas vacation. The Lent Term began on the 13th of January and ended on the second Friday before Easter. After the Easter vacation of three weeks, the Easter or Summer Term began on the 11th day after Easter Day and ended on the Friday after 'Commencement Day', which was the end of the academic year when students were awarded (commenced) their degrees. Commencement Day was always the first Tuesday in July. Then came the long vacation of three months. Students often remained in college over Christmas and Easter but were home or elsewhere for the long vacation. The poor roads made travel difficult, but to London there was a coach to the Bull Inn in Bishopsgate, formerly driven by Thomas Hobson. Hobson (of Hobson's choice but now only in recent memory) had developed the hire of riding horses (forty available) and conveyances and had built up a flourishing business. These services run by Hobson's successors were invaluable for travel not only between Cambridge and London but also to make many other journeys.

The daily routine of the students was intensive. At five o'clock, the chapel bell summoned them to hear the morning service, sometimes with a short address by a College Fellow. These devotions lasted an hour, after which came breakfast. The daily academic work was of two kinds : college and university. *College Studies* were attendance at lectures and 'examinations' by the tutors of the College, the subjects being Latin, Greek, Logic, Mathematics, and Philosophy. Distinct were *University Exercises,* consisting of lectures and disputations attended by students of all colleges in the Public Schools. This academic work occupied some four hours, after which the students dined in their colleges at midday. Then came another one or two hours of work either in College or the Public Schools, when they heard or participated in declamations or disputations of candidates for degrees. By mid-afternoon the students were at leisure except for attendance at the evening service in Chapel and supper at seven o'clock in Hall. The statutes of Christ's required all members to be in College after nine o'clock from Michaelmas to Easter and after ten o'clock from Easter to Michaelmas.

Evident from the above is the emphasis on training of the mind. Joseph Mede (1586-1638)[15] was at Christ's from 1602 to his death in 1638 (slightly before Power's time). His daily lectures in Humanity, Logic, and Philosophy were amplified by informal conversation with students as he met them in College. *Quid dubitas*, meaning 'what doubts have you encountered today?' he would ask, believing that not to doubt was not to understand. Mede was also a competent botanist and accompanied students into the 'backs' of the College and the fields nearby, identifying plants and distinguishing herbs of medical efficacy. Mede had an impediment of his speech and preferred his college fellowship to the several ecclesiastical positions which Archbishop Laud (1573-1645)[16] offered to him. William Chapell (1582-1649)[17] also at Christ's, excelled in the University in Latin logomancy and, when King James I visited Cambridge in 1615, Chapell defeated the King – and all other comers – in disputation.

To keep the undergraduates at academic work and to restrain all members of the College from undesirable pursuits, many forms of discipline had evolved.[18] For grave offences, such as contumacy (disobedience to authority), heresy, or violent behaviour, *Expulsion* from College and University could be invoked. The lesser penalty of *Rustication* was a temporary absence and, as so many days of residence were required for a degree, this might be a serious penalty. There were *Statutory Admonishments* sometimes requiring a public or written confession of the offence. Minor offences were inattention to studies or absences from chapel attendance.

Walling (confining to college) or *Gating* (confining in certain hours) were not particularly effective as students were usually in College during most of the weekdays. *Fining* only affected parents, as the young students often had no money. *Impositions* (e.g. writing portions of the Iliad) were frequently purchased. *Discommonisation* (loss of daily food) was harsh on impecunious students but did not punish those of wealthy parents. These objections to the above punishments explain why corporal punishment or its threat – of caning, birching or flogging – was used for students under eighteen years. Christ's had *Stocks* and there was the *Stang*, a pole to which the culprit was tied and carried around the College. All these corporal punishments were now less common than in the previous century, when students were even younger. It is probable that Henry was seldom admonished.

Power's medical studies were preceded by seven years in the Faculty of Arts, which period was divided into two parts. Tuition for admission to the BA degree occupied four years – the *quadriennium* of twelve terms of residence. Each year had appropriate studies and, in their last year, students were *Sophisters* and were entitled to partake in disputations. Towards and during their last term they were required to keep two *Acts* or *Responsions* and two *Opponencies* in the Public Schools, having earlier experienced these in their college. With a fortnight's notice of one of these, the student as a *Respondent* had to announce three propositions (usually moral or metaphysical), which he would debate in the Public Schools, beginning by reading a thesis in Latin before a *Moderator*, who would be a Master of Arts. His *Opponents* were three *Sophisters* from other colleges. The *Moderator* decided on the worth of the student's performance. After four of these debating sessions, his College would send him – if they considered him sufficiently prepared – as a *Quaestionist* for his three day final examination by the Proctors and Seniors in the Public Schools in the week before Ash Wednesday. If he passed, the College would send a *supplicat* to the Vice Chancellor and Senate praying for his admission *ad respondendum quaestioni*. There were yet more formal steps before the BA degree was granted. In Power's case he was awarded his BA in 1644 (Fig. 3.6). To advance to MA required three more years of study and participation in the academic debates described above. Power obtained his MA in 1648 but subsequently still had obligations to Cambridge during a *Regency* of five years, during which he participated in some of the Acts and Disputations described above. This period of three years, instruction between the BA and the MA and the subsequent five more years contrasts with today when tuition ceases after the BA is awarded.

Medical Studies at Cambridge

Power now began his studies towards his medical doctorate and, having gained his MA, he could proceed directly to an MD without the intervention of a BM. The *Statuta antiqua* – the Elizabethan Statutes of 1570 – required for the MD – after the period of the MA Regency – attendance at lectures for five years either at Cambridge, or some other approved university, two of which years were to be spent in the practice of clinical medicine. This requirement of clinical experience probably followed that in Montpellier, the first medical school to insist on clinical teaching. In researching Power's medical studies at Cambridge, we encounter a difficulty and a paradox. At the medical schools of, say, Montpellier, Paris, Padua, and Leiden, there are numerous professors in identified disciplines such as Medicine, Anatomy, Botany *etc.* whilst Cambridge had only two academic positions in medicine, namely : the Linacre lectureship attached to St. John's and founded by the will of Thomas Linacre (1460 ? – 1524)[19] in 1524, and the Regius Professorship of Physic founded by Henry VIII in 1540. A major difference between the medical tuition in Cambridge (and Oxford) and that in European medical schools is that much teaching took place in the colleges. Christ's, St John's, and Emmanuel all had several fellows with medical degrees and scientific interests and there were smaller numbers in other colleges. This complicates research into Power's tutors. The paradox is that, although there were only two academic positions in medicine, Cambridge in the 17th Century produced several distinguished physicians and scientists. Medical historians have frequently stated that, in the 17th Century, medical tuition in Cambridge (and Oxford) was so inadequate that most students sought tuition abroad. This is incorrect for both universities as was shown for Cambridge by Rook in a detailed study of the excellent records of Cambridge and Leiden.[20]

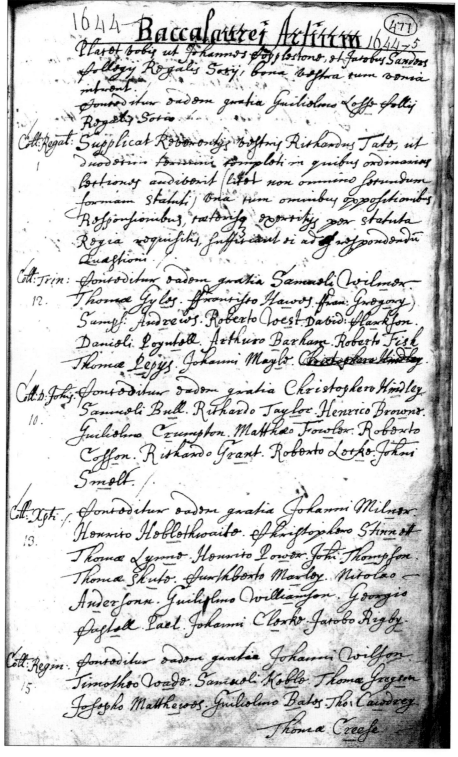

Figure 3.6 Cambridge University record in 1644 of Power's BA degree.

In the 17th Century, most medical students at Cambridge were taught there. Of those who went abroad, the interval between matriculation and conferment of a degree was often only a few weeks. These doctors merely sought a medical qualification of MD abroad, after which they would be granted an Oxbridge MD. It is interesting to compare the tuition of Thomas Browne at Oxford, Montpellier, Padua, and Leiden with the home tuition of Power, described above. Travel and tuition abroad, and especially visiting several medical schools, were desirable, but those who decided or had to remain at home did not fare badly. Power was fortunate in having in Glisson an outstanding Regius in Physic, in spite of Glisson's frequent absences in London.

Figure 3.7 Portrait of Francis Glisson.

Francis Glisson (1599?-1677)[21] (Fig. 3.7) entered Gonville and Caius in 1617, and was a fellow from 1624 to 1634 , when he gained his MD. In 1636 he was appointed Regius and remained in this post almost till his death.[22] Glisson was an outstanding physician and scientist, whose tuition greatly influenced Power, who read his books, some of which he possessed. Glisson's first published work was his *De rachitide sive morbo puerili*, which appeared in 1650 and was translated from Latin into English in 1651 by Philip Armin. Based on original observations, communicated and discussed by a group in London, it begins the scientific study of rickets. Glisson's most important work is his *Anatomia hepatis*, which appeared in 1654, and describes the normal and morbid appearance of the liver with the first description of the fibrous sheath of the portal tracts (Glisson's capsule). Glisson mainly resided in London and was active in the Royal College of Physicians, being a fellow from 1635, and president in 1667, 1668 and 1669, during which years his main preoccupation was financing the rebuilding of the College premises, destroyed in the 1666 Great Fire of London. He was also active in the formation of the Royal Society, of which he was a founder fellow. From about 1660 Glisson began the philosophical consideration of being, life and matter and in 1672 published *De natura substantiae energetica, seu, De vita naturae*. His views were challenged by the Cambridge Platonists, to be described below. In 1677, the year of his death, Glisson published *De ventriculo et intestinis*, a detailed account of the anatomy and physiology of the abdominal organs.

The Cambridge Platonists

Power's college in Cambridge and also Emmanuel College contained a group of thinkers which we identify as the 'Cambridge Platonists'. Previously only Francis Bacon (1561-1626)[23] had been a notable philosopher at Cambridge, but now, in the 17th century, was founded a new school of philosophy. The Cambridge Platonists viewed Christianity as a continuation of Platonic ideals. 'A good mind and a good life' was an underlying philosophy of Platonism, which was as much a religion as a philosophy. Platonic thought had passed to Christianity as a tradition, more Eastern than Western. Augustine could be considered a Neoplatonist before he became a Christian. What was valued in the writings of Plato was the acknowledgment of an eternal, invisible world, accounting for all things of sense, and a world in which it was correct to ask questions. The Cambridge Platonists also challenged current religious views and in particular the fanatical enthusiasm of Calvinism, the High Anglicanism of Laud, and the Erastianism of Thomas Hobbes (1588-1679).[24] They rejected predestination and that man was sinful since the Fall, believing that a person could, by the light of reason, move towards perfection. They shared the Puritan dislike of ritual, vestments, altar furnishings and stained glass but in this they were more tolerant – 'latitude men' – as was Milton. John Milton was at Christ's from February 1624/1625 to 1632.

Notable Platonists at Cambridge were Benjamin Whichcote (1609-1683)[25], Henry More (1614-1687) (Fig. 3.8)[26], Ralf Cudworth (1617-1680) (Fig. 3.9)[27], John Smith (1618-1652)[28], and Nathaniel Culverwell (1619-1651) [29]. Of these, More and Cudworth at Christ's would be well known to Power and he would meet the others at Emmanuel. Another important academic influence was that the Platonists communicated with academics on the European Continent, notably Decartes, and this directed Power to an interest in science, both natural philosophy (Botany and Zoology), experimental philosophy (experimental science), and the use of the microscope and telescope.

Henry More (fig. 3.5) was born in Grantham and went to school at Eton from which he proceeded to Cambridge. He entered Christ's in 1631 as a student and, becoming a Fellow, remained there till his death in 1687. He was

Figure 3.8 Portrait of Henry More. Engraving forming the frontispiece of More's *Opera Omnia*.

Figure 3.9 Portrait of Ralf Cudworth from a drawing by David Loggan in 1684.

the first of the Cambridge Platonists and his association with Christ's for the whole of his adult life earned him the name 'The Angel of Christ's'. More was a reader rather than a teacher and a writer rather than a preacher. He was friend of Lord and Lady Conway and his contact with that family is recorded in *The Conway Letters*.[30] Ralf Cudworth was the greatest of the Cambridge Platonists, surpassing John Smith as a preacher and having a more profound philosophy than that of More. From a school in Somerset he entered Emmanuel College in 1632 and, at the age of 27 years, he was elected Master of Clare. He became Professor of Hebrew and, in 1654, Master of Christ's, which position he held for over thirty years. His major work, *The True Intellectual System of the Universe* (1678), directly challenged Hobbes.

The University of Cambridge at the time of Power's stay (1641-1655) was disturbed by the Civil Wars, ending in the execution of the King (1649) and the creation of the Protectorate.[31] The colleges of Cambridge were purged by the Earl of Manchester – Commander of the Parliamentary forces - who, in March 1643/4 removed nine masters from the headships of their colleges. At Christ's, Thomas Bainbridge was allowed to remain, but nine fellows were ejected, amongst them William Power, Henry's uncle. The disruption to the College is evident by the numbers of admissions: 27 in 1641-2, but 15 in 1642-3, and only 12 in 1643-4. In 1644-5 numbers had returned to 58, and in 1645-6, there were 52 admissions.[32]

Power was an excellent student of medicine in a University and at a College that provided, despite the disturbances of the Civil Wars, a thorough grounding in medicine and also an introduction to the new sciences, whose discoveries were known in Cambridge through many academic contacts. That Power profited from these is evident by his letter to Thomas Browne dated 15th September, 1648 :

> Sr, I have now by the frequency of living and dead dissections of Doggs, run through the whole body of Anatomy Insisting on Spigelius, Bartholinus, Fernelius, Columbus, Veslingius, but especially Harvey's Circulatio, & the two Incomparable Authors, Descartes, & Regius[33]

His studies were enlarged by the acquisition of a comprehensive library, modelled on that of Dr Browne.[34]

That Power gained his MD in 1654 is shown by his entry in the University Grace Book (Fig. 3.10), which is dated 5 July. This is the 'supplicat' required for the award of the 'grace' for the degree. The Latin text is as follows :

> *Supplicat Reverentiis vestries Henricus Power ut studium septem annorum in medicina, postquam rexerit in artibus, in quibus lectiones ordinarias*

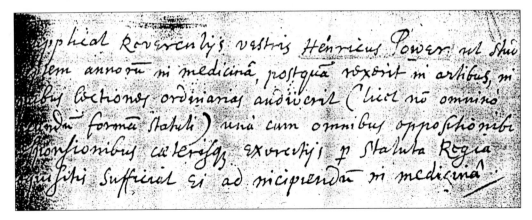

Figure 3.10 Entry in the Cambridge University Grace Book of the 'supplicat' dated July 5th. This was the preliminary to the award of a grace for Power's MD. The Praelector of Christ's College (William Outram) attests that all academic and residential requirements have been met.

audiverit (licet non [?] omnino secundum formam statuti) una cum omnibus oppositionibus responsionibus caeterisque exercitiis per Statuta Regia sequi sitis sufficiat ei ad incipiendum in medicina.

In English :

Henry Power supplicates to your reverences that he has studied medicine for seven years, after which he will have ruled in arts, in which he will have heard ordinary lectures (it is [not] entirely allowed in accordance with the form of the statute) together with all responses to opponents and other exercises according to the royal statutes you may follow, is sufficient for him to incept in medicine.

The MD, being a higher degree, was usually awarded at Commencement, the festival ending the academic year on the first Tuesday in July. On 4 July 1654, Henry Power qualified as a physician.

NOTES AND REFERENCES

1 Power matriculated in 1641 and remained under the supervision of the University until he gained his doctorate of medicine in 1655.
2 The following references describe the University, Christ's College, the Medical School, and many of the senior staff in the time of Power's education at Cambridge.
3 Masson, D. *The Life of John Milton : narrated in connection with the Political, Ecclesiastical and Literary History of His Time.* In 6 volumes. London : Macmillan & Co, 1881. Volume I, p. 111-145, describes Christ's

College and Cambridge University during the residence of Milton from 1625 to 1632. Masson gives many references to primary sources.

4   Peile, J. *Christ's College*. London : F.E. Robinson & Co, 1900.

5   Peile, J. *Biographical Register of Christ's College, 1505-1905 and of the earlier Foundation, God's House, 1448-1505*. In 6 volumes. Cambridge, Cambridge University Press, 1910. Volume I covers 1448-1665.

6   Rouse Ball, W.W. *Cambridge Papers*. London : Macmillan & Co, 1918.

7   Venn, J. & Venn, J.A. *Alumni Cantabrigienses*. Cambridge : Cambridge University Press, 1924.

8   Rolleston, H.D. *The Cambridge Medical School : A Biographical History*. Cambridge : Cambridge University Press, 1932.

9   Rook, A. 'Medicine in Cambridge 1660-1760', *Medical History*, (1969), 13, pp. 107-122.

10 Rook, A., editor. *Cambridge and its Contribution to Medicine*. Proceedings of the Seventh British Congress on the History of Medicine, University of Cambridge, 10th - 13th September, 1969. London : Wellcome Institute of the History of Medicine, 1971.

11 *Oxford Dictionary of National Biography* (henceforth *ODNB*). Oxford : Oxford University Press, 2004.

12 I have used the modern calendar year of 1641. Until 1752 the year in England began on March 25th.

13 Henry Power may have had some of his schooling in York but evidence is lacking.

14 David Loggan, *ODNB*, 34, pp. 321-322.

15 Joseph Mede [Mead], *ODNB*, 37, pp. 683-685.

16 William Laud, *ODNB*, 32, pp. 655-670.

17 William Chappel, *ODNB*, 11, pp. 76-78.

18 Rouse Ball, *ODNB*, 12, pp. 194-224.

19 Thomas Linacre, *ODNB*, 33, pp. 803-806.

20 Rook, 1971, pp. 58-62.

21 Francis Glisson, *ODNB*, 22, pp. 473-475.

22 Glisson's absences from Cambridge have been criticised but it seems that the salary of the Regius Chair was seldom paid until restored by Cromwell during the Protectorate.

23 Francis Bacon, *ODNB*, 3, 123-145.

24 Thomas Hobbes, *ODNB*, 27, pp. 385-395.

25 Benjamin Whichcote, *ODNB*, 58, pp. 472-474.

26 Henry More, *ODNB*, 39, pp. 47-50.

27 Ralf Cudworth, *ODNB*, 14, pp. 562-565.

28 John Smith, *ODNB*, 51, pp. 200-201.

29 Nathaniel Culverwell, *ODNB*, 14, 612-613.
30 *The Conway Letters : the Correspondence of Anne, Vicountess Conway, Henry More, and their Friends, 1642-1684.* Edited by Majorie Hope Nicolson. Revised edition by Sarah Hutton, Oxford, Clarendon Press, 1992.
31 Peile, 1900, pp. 160-175.
32 Peile, 1900, p. 165.
33 Letter to Dr Browne, 15 September, 1648. *BL, MS Sloane 1911-1913, f.80.* Reproduced in G. Keynes, *The Works of Sir Thomas Browne*, vols 1-6, (London, Faber and Gwyer, becoming Faber and Faber. 1928-31), 6, p. 283.
34 The Catalogue of 'all my books' before Power's move from Halifax to Wakefield in 1664. British Library, *Sloane MS. 1346.*

Chapter 4

Halifax in the 17th century. Marriage and Family.
Residence in New Hall, Elland. Move to Wakefield.

After an excellent and prolonged education at Cambridge, Henry Power returned to his native Yorkshire where he remained for the remainder of his life. Halifax was a small but prosperous town important to and benefiting from the wool trade.

Halifax in the 17th Century[1 2 3 4 5 6 7 8]

Halifax on the river Calder in the West Riding is to the south of what we now call the Yorkshire Dales. East of the Pennines the limestone hills are parted by valleys created by rivers and streams, running from west to east and finding their way into the river Humber. The Vikings found these rivers an easy route inland and made many settlements. The whole landscape is of great natural beauty, for the preservation of which several national parks have been designated. The 1749 map in Figure 4.1 indicates how its geography – dominated by rivers – might have been viewed by the local people. The size of the lettering corresponds to the importance of Halifax compared with Leeds, Doncaster and Rotherham. The river Calder, arising from a spring at Giggleswich, is joined by the river Hebden at Halifax. Daniel Defoe, in his tour of Great Britain, describes the interest and enchantment of Halifax in the early part of the 17th century.[9] Halifax was at the centre of the woollen industry in England and everywhere there were steep hills and deep valleys, where streams were diverted into rills of running water turning small mills, before flowing into the river Calder. Underground there was coal for fuel. The woollen industry was composed of small houses close together, each being a 'manufactury', where a family lived and worked. The women and children carded and spun the wool, which the men wove into cloth. The cloth, when dyed, was put out to dry on 'tenters' in the sun. Defoe commented on the kaleidoscope of these numerous sheets dyed in various colours. The dyed pieces of cloth displayed in the open might have invited theft were it not for the local Halifax laws. The first history of Halifax by a Dr Samuel Midgely describes the Draconian treatment of miscreants in Halifax, which prompted their prayer 'From Hell, Hull, and Halifax, Good Lord deliver us'. Stealing goods valued at more than thirteen pence and one half–penny incurred the death penalty. The title page and frontispiece of the1712 edition of Midgely's book is reproduced in Figure 4.2. The frontispiece is a chilling depiction of the method of execution in Halifax, which anticipated the introduction of Dr Guillotin's decapitating instrument, not introduced until

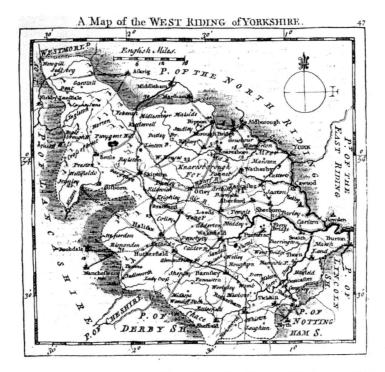

Figure 4.1 Map of West Riding drawn by Thomas Kitchin in 1749.

1791. Woollen manufacture continued the prosperity of Halifax in the 17th century. Figure 4.3 shows a view of the town and Figure 4.4 a plan of the town in the 18th century. The church is shown in figure 4.5 whilst Figures 4.5 and 4.6 depict old houses that survived into the early 19th century. Whilst there are few seventeenth century views of Halifax, the large house of New Hall occupied by Henry and his wife has survived. There were many other notable houses occupied by families who were Henry's patients. Journeys, however, were not easy and Henry's visits to patients were on horseback rather that by carriage. John Ogilby's *Brittania* of 1675 shows a prominent road through Halifax from Richmond in the north to Oakeham in the south.[10] At Halifax, this road crossed a road from Manchester in the west to Wakefield and Pontefract in the east. Immediately to the north were two smaller easterly directed roads, one to Southoram and another to Northoram, the latter being that to Hipperholme. Since the dissolution of the monasteries, roads had been neglected, and in wet weather the muddy tracts were impassable to wagons. The preferred transport was a train of pack animals traversing a narrow paved strip called a 'causey'.[11] Today a paved '*Magna Via*' from Halifax to Hipperhome survives. Travel into Halifax remained difficult even in the 18th century except in very dry or very cold (frozen) weather. Access was easier from the north, which single entrance gave an insularity to the town.

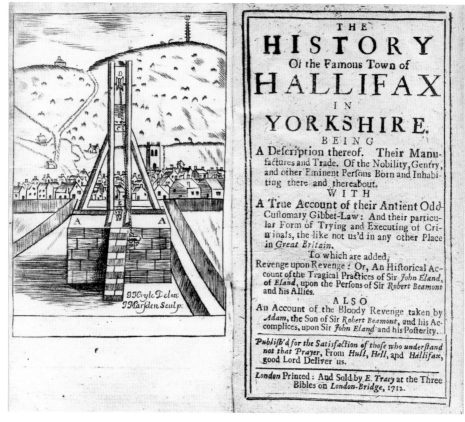

Figure 4.2 Frontispiece of the 1712 edition of *History of Halifax* by Samiel Midgely.

Figure 4.3 Engraving in Watson, T. *The Antiquities of the Town of Halifax in Yorkshire,* 1775. The view is of Halifax from the South East.

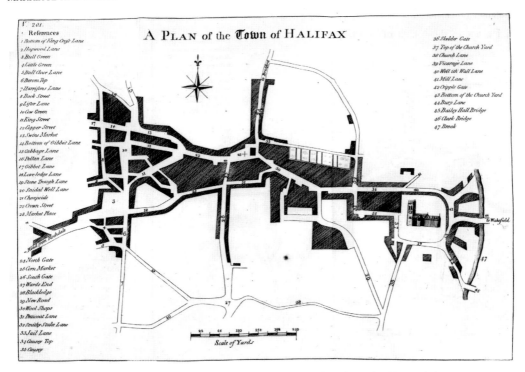

A PLAN of the Town of HALIFAX

V. 201.

References

1 Bottom of King Crofs Lane
2 Hopwood Lane
3 Bull Green
4 Little Green
5 Bull Close Lane
6 Barom Top
7 Harrifons Lane
8 Back Street
9 Lifter Lane
10 Cow Green
11 King Street
12 Copper Street
13 Swine Market
14 Bottom of Gibbet Lane
15 Cabbage Lane
16 Pellon Lane
17 Gibbet Lane
18 Love-ledge Lane
19 Stone Trough Lane
20 Snidal Well Lane
21 Cheapside
22 Crown Street
23 Market Place

24 North Gate
25 Corn Market
26 South Gate
27 Wards End
28 Blackledge
29 New Road
30 Wool Shops
31 Petticoat Lane
32 Smithy Stake Lane
33 Jail Lane
34 Causey Top
35 Causey

36 Skeldar Gate
37 Top of the Church Yard
38 Church Lane
39 Vicarage Lane
40 Well ith Wall Lane
41 Mill Lane
42 Cripple Gate
43 Bottom of the Church Yard
44 Bury Lane
45 Bailey Hall Bridge
46 Clark Bridge
47 Brook

Scale of Yards

Figure 4.4 Plan of the Town of Halifax. Note the church in the East of the town.

A South East Prospect of HALIFAX CHURCH

Figure 4.5 Halifax Church seen from the South East.

Figure 4.6 Houses in Northgate as they might have appeared in the eighteenth century. This area was demolished in 1824.

Marriage and Family

Henry Power had spent most of his childhood and all of his school days in Halifax.

His father had died when he was twelve and his mother had remarried. Both his mother and his stepfather were well off and there was no financial problem in completing his education at school and arranging his admission to Cambridge. The family tradition – usually for clerical training – was to attend Christ's College, where Henry remained during term time from his admission in 1641 to the award of his final degree of MD in 1655. He returned to his family home for all of the summer vacations and possibly for some of the Easter and Christmas breaks. After his graduation as an MA, his medical studies kept him in Cambridge during term time from 1648 to 1655, but gradually he was spending more time at home in Halifax. He was also preparing to establish himself in medical practice. It was an excellent opportunity. Throughout his career Power had no rival in Halifax as a physician holding a doctorate of medicine. But he needed a wife and a commodious house from which to conduct his medical practice. He was also eager for facilities to continue the scientific experiments which he had begun at Cambridge. He was interested in botany, zoology, microscopy, and astronomy. Henry was now a young man, ready to plan and carry out his objectives.[12] He soon attained his requirements, of a wife and a house. His chosen bride was Margery (or Margerie) Foxcroft. Their confusing relation to each other requires a detailed description. Margery Foxcroft was born in Halifax, where on the 20th of March she was baptised.[13] She was the daughter of Anthony Foxcroft by his first wife, a Margery Hovenden. Henry's father, John Power, lived in the Mulcture Hall, which he had built in 1631.[14] He died in 1638 and there is a record of his burial in May in Halifax church. His will was proved on 18th February, 1638/1639, by his widow, Jane, together with Anthony Foxcroft, after which Jane married Anthony on the 26th March, 1639. Anthony Foxcroft was a cloth importer and on his first marriage in 1630, his father-in-law, the Reverend Charles Greenwood, assisted him financially to purchase Woodhouse, Scar Bottom, where he lived with his new wife and their daughter, Margery, born in 1633. When his father died in 1636, Anthony became the owner of New Hall, Elland. His first wife died, and when he married Jane, they moved into New Hall with Margery, then six years old, together with Henry, his stepson. Then, several years later, Henry had chosen to marry Margery, a stepson marrying a stepdaughter. The complication concerning the house was that some years before, Anthony had leased New Hall for 1,000 years to the Reverend Greenwood, who was now deceased, but had bequeathed the house to Margery. Anthony had been living for several years in a house that belonged to his daughter.[15] Anthony Foxcroft and a Thomas Radcliffe had been the executors of the will of Greenwood and Anthony Foxcroft had assumed possession of the house, which really belonged to his daughter and now through marriage to Henry. To gain possession by Henry and his wife required litigation. There was a protracted legal wrangle heard in London, the litigants attending in December, 1656, and in February and June, 1657. The case was decided for Power. New Hall became his residence and that of his wife from 1659 until their death some years later.

On 1 May, 1658, before they were living at New Hall, a daughter was born to Henry and Margaret, and she was baptised Ellen on 25 May, at Elland.[16] Ellen married into the Lister family. In 1659, on 30 November, George was born and was baptised, also at Elland on 19 June, 1660. In 1664 there was another daughter, Jane, baptised at Elland on 11th August.

New Hall, Elland, Halifax

New Hall figured greatly in Power's adult life, being the base for his medical practice and also where he conducted his observations and scientific experiments, when this activity moved from Cambridge to Halifax. New Hall, Elland, is described today as a 'Pennine Gentry House', and remains in a fine state of preservation, not greatly altered since Power's residence (Figs 4.7 & 4.8). Even then it was an old dwelling. Since the 12th century, there had been a substantial residence in Elland cum Greetland, an ancient settlement on the south side of the river Calder flowing eastwards from the high ground of the Pennines. By the middle of the 14th century, this old Hall was owned by the Saville family. There were many branches of the Saville family and we know from the autobiography of Sir John Saville (1546–1607) of Methley that the Hullen Edge branch of the Savilles built the New Hall. It was Sir John's great-grandfather, Nicholas, the younger son of Thomas from Hollingedge who built the Hall. As Nicholas was born *circa* 1460, the Hall must have been built towards the end of the fifteenth century. The house became the dwelling of a minor branch of the great family of Savilles, prominent in the West Riding of Yorkshire.

Figure 4.7 Old buildings in Halifax.

Figure 4.8 North aspect of New Hall, Elland.

For the plan and construction of New Hall, I am indebted to the researches and writing of Colum Giles.[17] The Hall was designed and built in the manner of several old houses of about the same period in the Calder valley, the survival of which delight historians of domestic architecture. The centre of the house was a large square hall, open from the ground to the roof. There was a western bay, which enlarged the body of the Hall into the major room of the house. In the eastern bay was located the means of heating which, in West Yorkshire, might be one of three constructions. A stone chimney (uncommon) might be built, or an open hearth would require an opening in the roof for the smoke to escape. In the case of New Hall, as with many houses in the late medieval period, the smoke from the fire was directed through a timber and plaster flue, which was called a fire-hood or smoke-hood. These were large structures which, though removed in later modernisations, left traces of the original method for the escape of smoke. New Hall was built to accommodate a large fire–hood in the hall, which dominated a large area of the hall and above created a small room around and behind the fire-hood. The open hall was the main room of the medieval house and used for dining and entertaining. It communicated with east and west wings of rooms on two storeys. The kitchen would have been an adjacent or a separate structure, the remains of which have not survived. Such was the medieval house that Henry and Margery Power gained after the prolonged lawsuit described above.

We know from Power's papers that he was the legal owner of New Hall in December 1656, but he and Margaret did not live there until early 1659. From August 1649 to November 1658 Power's letters are addressed as: from Halifax. His next letter dated May 10th 1659 to Dr Thomas Browne was from New Hall, as were all his subsequent letters. We can infer that Henry and Margaret moved into New Hall in the first half of 1659. Power made extensive improvements and alterations to the house, the accounts of which are preserved in his manuscript collections in the British Library. I am indebted to their analysis by Jennifer Stead.[18] Power's medical practice and his scientific experiments and observations made from this house will be described in chapters 5-8.

Figure 4.9 Interior of New Hall, Elland.
The open hall on the ground floor is the principal room of the house.

Move to Wakefield

Why in 1664 Power, from living in a house much altered to his liking, should move to Wakefield can only be surmised.[19] Clay suggests:

> Having got good customers among the surrounding gentry, who, perhaps, were more numerous than in the Halifax district, it would be more convenient for him.

His Memorandum Book notes his move:

> ... that I came to Wakefield to live 7 of October 1664 wch was on a Friday.

Whilst it is certain that the family moved to Wakefield on this date, it seems that, as early as 1663, he had financial obligations in Wakefield, as evident by his contributions to the local militia. The *1662 Militia Act of 13 & 14 Charles II, c.3* had been enacted. Previous arrangements of charging the cost of arms, powder, and training of the local militia to the 'constable's lay' were replaced by this act. All persons whose annual income reached £ 500 were compelled to provide a horseman, whilst those with lesser incomes had to fund one foot soldier for every £ 50 of annual income. Power's annual income from his estate and professional fees was between £ 100 and £ 200 and he had to provide for two soldiers, as his accounts show :

> **July, 1663**. The charges of my foot arms since the setting of the new militia.
> A musket and new stocking of it 12 0
> Bandoliers sword and new scabbard ... .13 8
> new sword belt 3 4
> knapsack 2 8
> Head piece 6 0
> 1 day's appearance at Nunbrooke about the end of July last, 1663. 1 6
> 4 August, 3 days training at Almondbury 3 0
> For match and powder then 1 0
> For advance money 25 0
> 3 days training at Almondbury, 1st Oct., and
> for match and powder 4 0
> 10 days appearing at Wakefield and Pontefract 10 0
> **1665**. the account of my foot arms :
> for 3 days training at Almondbury and
> Whitley Hall at 18d. per day 4 6
> given then to muster master 5 Feb., 1665,

for 6 days pay here at Wakefield at 16d. per day. 8 0
8 Feb. to the drummer for listing my new souldier John Huther
instead of Akerley... 6
given by me to my new man 1 0
Paid 1st May to Sam Yeates in Ealand for a firelock 6 0

In the same year of 1662, the Hearth Tax came into operation, a very unpopular
levy, but of inestimable value to historians, as the Hearth Tax Rolls of Wakefield
demonstrate. For 1664-1665, 351 persons paid for 1160 hearths, the charge
being 2 shillings per hearth. Henry Power recorded his payments of this tax
over several years together with sundry other payments, which, for 1666,
totalled £ 8 9s 7d . The breakdown of his expenses may be seen from an extract
of his Memoranda Book :

	£	s	d
To sub collectors for poll money	5	0	0
For my wife		3	0
2 servants		7	0
chimney money (half year)		8	0
to vicar for whole years gratuity		10	0
to the clerk		1	6
mending of highways		4	0
Royal aid		3	6
Poor rate		4	8
Constable lays		3	6
Hearth money (half year)		11	0
Church lays		4	8
Constable lays at 3d per £ on £35		8	9
Total	8	9	7

From 1664, the entries of visits, prescriptions, and fees continue but are more
directed to patients around Wakefield. Accounts of repairs and alterations
switch to his house in Wakefield, which, it seems from his hearth taxes, was
large. There is evidence in his letters that he was now in poor health, which
might explain his move to Wakefield, a gentler area than the robust Calderdale
valley. His lucrative practice continued but his scientific experiments ceased, as
did his researches into botany and zoology.

Power's death and descendants

Henry died in 1668, and was buried on 23 December, in All Saints, Wakefield
Parish Church (Figs. 4.10, 4.11, 4.12 & 4.13), now Wakefield Cathedral.[20]

Figure 4.10 Plan of Wakefield in the Seventeenth Century.

His will, drawn up on 19 December, 1668, was proved on 2 June, 1669, by his widow. Margery remained in the house in Wakefield for a further eight years, returning to Halifax on 6 December, 1676. Her son, George, was now sixteen, and he inherited New Hall, when he came of age. There is evidence that he moved into the house in 1681, with a child and a lady who was not his wife. George lived an irregular and unremunerative life and, in 1686, he was in court from an incident in an ale-house in Elland, kept by a William Taylor, whose wife he had attempted to rape or, at least, molest.[21] George died in 1700 and was buried on the 10th May at Elland. He was unmarried and had no legal heirs. His will, dated 3rd May, 1700, was proved at York on the 5th of April, 1701, the sole executor being John Hanson, who inherited New Hall and sundry other properties in Elland. John Hanson of Southowram is described in the will as 'my kinsman'. A bequest of '£20 to Elizabeth Lister, my Niece' was presumably to the daughter of his sister Ellen. New Hall now passed through several owners, but survived to be restored in the present century. It is now a private residence. With the death of George, the line of Henry Power was extinguished, further obscuring the memory of Power. But his memorial plaque, in what is now Wakefield Cathedral, reminds us of a great physician and scientist, who practiced in Halifax and Wakefield.

Figure 4.11 South West view of All Saints Church, Wakefield. The engraving is dated 1834.

Figure 4.12 South Porch of All Saints Church, Wakefield, as seen in 1824.

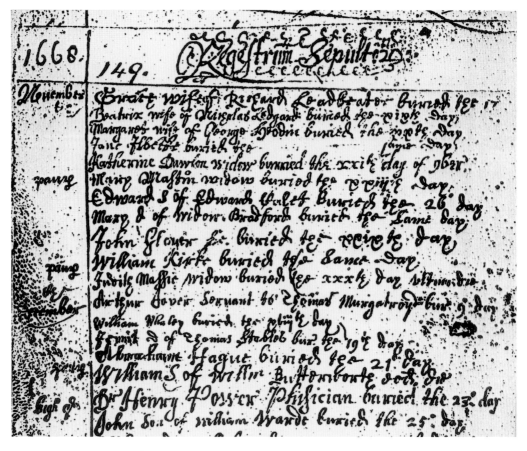

Figure 4.13 Entry in the Register of Power's burial at Wakefield on 23rd December, 1668.

NOTES AND REFERENCES

1 References 2-7 describe Halifax in the 17th Century.

2 Midgely, S. *Hallifax and its Gibbet-Law Placed in a true Light*, printed by J. How for William Bentley, Hallifax, 1708. Further editions appeared in 1712, 1761, and 1789, and in 1886 a reprint of the 1708 edition was made by J.H. Turner of Bradford.

3 Wright, T. *The Antiquities of the Town of Halifax in Yorkshire.* London, Halifax & Wakefield, James Hodgson, 1738.

4 Watson, J. *The History and Antiquities of the Parish of Halifax in Yorkshire.* London : T. Lowndes, 1775. Facsimile. Didsbury, Manchester : E.J. Morten, 1973.

5 Wright, T. *The Antiquities of the Town of Halifax in Yorkshire*, etc. Leeds: James Lister, 1738. Reprint edited by J.H. Turner, Bingley : T. Harrison, 1884.

6   Watson, J. *Biographia Halifaxiensis or Halifax Families and Worthies*. Bingley : J.H. Turner, 1883. This is the biographical portion of Watson's 1775 *History* compiled by J.H. Turner.

7   Garside, M.W. 'The Social History of Halifax in the Seventeenth Century'. *Transactions of the Halifax Antiquarian Society*, 1923 [no volume number], pp. 65-100.

8   Hanson, T.W. *Halifax Street Lore*. Halifax, William Patterson, 1932.

9   A Gentleman [Daniel Defoe]. *A Tour through the whole Island of Great Britain*, volume 3. London : [Publisher] ,1724-1727, pp. 97-114.

10 Ogilby, J. *Britannia*. London : 1675.

11 Clegg, C. 'Coaching Days', *Transactions of the Halifax Antiquarian Society*, 1923 [no volume number], pp. 123-158.

12 Clay, J.W. 'Dr Henry Power, of New Hall, FRS'. *Papers, Reports, etc. read to the Halifax Antiquarian Society*, 1917, pp, 1-31. [No volume number. Later became the *Transactions*.] A full account of Henry Power with copies of the wills of John Power, Henry Power and George Power.

13 Clay, p. 7.

14 The Mulcture Hall survives today but has an added storey of brick. The original doorway bears the date 1631. Inside there is a plaster ceiling with a medallion with the inscription I.P. 1637. The mulcture was the measure that the Lord's miller dipped into a sack of corn to take out the portion due to the manor.

15 Clay, pp. 8-11. Gives details of the case of Radcliffe versus Power.

16 Clay, p. 7. Gives details of Ellen, George and Jane Power.

17 Giles, C. 'New Hall, Elland; the story of a Pennine Gentry House from *c.* 1490 to the mid-19th century'. In *Old West Riding*, vol. 1, no. 2. Ed. G. Redmonds, Oldgate, Huddersfield : [Publisher] , 1981).

18 Stead, J. Dr Henry Power and his alterations at New Hall, Elland 1656-1664. In Old West Riding, edited by Jennifer Stead, Old West Riding Books, Huddersfield : [Publisher], vol. 8, no. 2, 1988.

19 Wright, 1738, no page number.

20 Clay, p. 7.

21 Redmonds, G. *Huddersfield and District under the Stuarts : Seventy years of law and disorder*. G.R. Books, Lepton, Huddersfield, 1985, pp. 26-27.

Chapter 5

Mercurial Experiments. The Royal Society.
Collaboration with Richard Towneley.

In the early part of the 17th century, scientists in continental Europe were performing experiments and making observations in chemistry and physics. Their scientific discoveries were communicated to individuals in England, commonly located in London, Oxford and Cambridge. At the time of Power's medical studies, the Cambridge scientists frequently corresponded with those of France, and especially with Descartes. Important in Paris was Father Marin Mersenne, who excelled as a collector and disseminator of research findings. His voluminous correspondence has survived and has been published.[1] From several sources, Power became acquainted with the observations on the vacuum that can be created above a column of mercury, which discovery is generally attributed to Torricelli of Florence. This can be regarded as the midpoint of the expansion of knowledge of a vacuum and of air pressure. The scientists in Cambridge (and in Oxford and London) were intrigued with the various experiments on the mercury column and the vacuum above. Power observed these experiments, repeated them in Cambridge and then performed an extensive series of experiments at his home in Halifax. His contribution to these researches was to use a mercury column as a barometer to measure air pressure and then to use the barometer as an altimeter.

Experiments in Renaissance Europe [2][3][4]

In the early seventeenth century, the existence of a vacuum, postulated by Democritus but denied by Aristotle, was gaining acceptance, despite the objections of the Catholic Church. Democritus believed that a space, if devoid of any material body, would then be a void or a *vacuum coacervatum*. There could be degrees of emptiness of a space, which proportions corresponded to density. Aristotle denied the existence of a vacuum and propounded elaborate arguments as to why the motion of bodies and the perception of beams of light required a continuous medium for transmission. Aristotle's *Physics* and his *De Anima* contain these beliefs.[5] Important for our subject is the debate whether air had weight, could exert pressure, and could be compressed. By 1612, Galileo had come to believe in the possibility of a vacuum, but he did not believe that air had weight and could exert pressure. There were current practical observations on how much rise of a liquid was possible in a siphon and the maximum height of water attainable with a suction pump. In 1615, Galileo wrote (translated): 'the air in itself and above the water weighs nothing'.[6] The first important research that questioned why there was a maximum height of water in the use of a suction pump, was made in France by Isaac Beeckman (1588–1637), descended from a Cornelius Beeckman originally from Cologne but coming from the Low Countries.[7] Working in Caen, Beeckman studied the effect of air pressure on the action of a suction pump. His research and conclusions were presented in an MD thesis to the University of Caen. An incomplete copy of this thesis survives in the British Library.[8] In his journal he wrote (translated from Latin) 'air, after the manner of water, presses on things and compresses them according to the depth of the superincumbent air'.[9] At the end of the first quarter of the seventeenth century, this was a convincing statement that air had weight and could exert pressure. On 1st October 1629, Beeckman communicated his findings to Father Marin Mersenne in Paris.[10] Mersenne's collection and dissemination of research findings was the 'internet' of the 17th Century. Other researchers in France, e.g. Jean Rey, had arrived at this fundamental belief : that air had weight and could exert pressure.[11]

We now come to decisive research in Italy. In Genoa, Giovanni Batista Baliani (1582-1666) observed that a siphon would not carry water over a hill which was more than twenty-one metres above the supplying reservoir. If a siphon in such a position was filled with water and the ends opened, the water level dropped to about ten metres below the level of the supplying reservoir. On 27th July 1630, Baliani wrote to Galileo asking for his explanation of this phenomenon, which was known to many persons engaged in supplying water from reservoirs. Baliani wrote with deferential courtesy – he was addressing the greatest living scientist – and Galileo replied promptly on 6th August.[12] His explanation was curious : a vacuum could have a force (*forza o resistenza del vacuo*). Galileo believed that a column of water had tensile strength, as did a pillar of stone or a beam of wood.[13] As the length of the water column increased, its weight exceeded its strength, and the column parted. Baliani was not satisfied with Galileo's reply, and wrote again at length on the 4th October, but received no elaboration of the explanation made by this great scientist.[14] So, the measurement of the possible height of the water rising above some high ground on its way from the reservoir had been the subject of enquiry in Italy by Baliani, whilst in France the limit of the height of water in a suction pump had been measured in Caen by Beeckman. Both these figures were roughly the same but neither of the two researchers was aware of the other investigator.

The next advance, of great importance, took place in Rome among a group of scientists which included Raffael Magiotti (1597-1658), Evangelista Torricelli (1608-1647) and Gasparo Berti (16??-1643?). These scientists had seen Galileo's *Discorsi*, which was published in 1638, and had read the account from Baliani and Galileo's reply. Of these three scientists, it was Gasparo Berti who planned and executed a memorable experiment. Berti, from Mantua, was a mathematician and astronomer. He was a modest retiring young man, who has left very few writings. It is extraordinary that he has no mention in the *Italian Biographical Index* (Munich, 1993), which combines entries from 321 Italian biographical reference works. This obscure scientist deserves more than a mention in the history of science as he conducted an experiment of great importance in physics. Fortunately there are four accounts, of which the most accurate is that of Emmanuel Maignan (1601-1676), who taught at the Convent on Monte Pincio in Rome. Some years later, Maignan, on returning to his native Toulouse, wrote a long treatise on natural philosophy, which includes an account of the experiment.[15] The lack of a contemporary description is explained by the hostility of the Church to statements that did not agree with its teaching. Discussion of the nature of air had to agree with Aristotle. When the mere existence of a vacuum was denied, it was better to leave unrecorded an experiment which claimed to have created a vacuum. Gaspar Berti erected a leaden tube outside the wall of his house, the upper end opposite a window, and the lower end in water contained in a cask on the ground. The tube was filled with water held by two brass taps, one at the bottom of the tube and the other at the top of the tube. Opening the brass taps allowed the water to attain a natural level, which was observed in a glass flask attached to the top of the tube. The height of the water column was about 18 cubits. Berti and his colleagues had produced a vacuum, a concept denied by the Catholic Church. The date of this experiment may be inferred from a letter dated 12th March 1648 from Magiotti in Rome to Mersenne in Paris.[16] This includes the phrase (translated from Italian) : 'Berti believed that he could convince Galileo with this experiment'.[17] So Galileo was still alive. The experiment must have preceded Galileo's death on 8th January, 1642. The date of the experiment was probably 1641, the same year that Power matriculated at Cambridge.

Another observer of Berti's experiment in Rome was Torricelli who, in Florence, planned a similar experiment using a glass tube filled with mercury. The use of mercury arose from a suggestion of Galileo, which had been noted[18] by Vincenso Viviani (1622-1703), a colleague of Torricelli in Florence. A copy of Galileo's 1638 *Discorsi* in Florence has marginal notes in the hand of Viviani at the place where Galileo writes (translated) :

And it is my belief that the same result will follow in other liquids, such as quicksilver ... in which the rupture will take place to a lesser or greater height than 18 cubits, according to the ... specific gravity of these liquids.[19]

Galileo still thought that a column of water or another liquid had a limited length. His explanation was that as the length increased it would reach a point where the 'strength' of the water would not bear the weight of the column. Whilst his fellow scientists demurred, they did understand that the specific gravity of the liquid would determine the possible length of a column of liquid. This turned their attention to the use of the heaviest liquid known : mercury. The experiment used a glass tube, about 3 feet long and closed at one end. When filled with mercury and inverted into a small bath of mercury, the level in the tube fell to 29 inches and above was the space : the vacuum. The first mercury experiments are ascribed to Torricelli, but Viviani had the tubes constructed, obtained the mercury and performed the experiments, probably in 1644.[20] However, Torricelli is rightly considered to have designed the experiment and to have invented the barometer. His correspondence with Michelangelo Ricci in Rome reveals an advanced knowledge of the experiment and the future uses of the mercury column, which he called an instrument.[21] From this date, Torricelli of Florence receives most of the credit for the creation and discovery of a vacuum, eclipsing the pioneer experiment of Berti in Rome.

Experiments on barometric pressure in France

In spite of Torricelli's experiment, disbelief in the existence of a vacuum persisted among many scientists, including Mersenne in Paris. The experiments of Torricelli had become generally known in France, probably from the traveller Balthasar de Monconys (1611-1665)[22]. In 1645, Mersenne made a visit to Florence to see the mercury experiment. Pierre Petit (1589-1677) performed the first experiment in France, at Rouen in 1646. Petit was the engineer in charge of the fortifications at Rouen.[23] Etienne Noël now devised experiments, in which air and water were introduced into the 'space'. Although they had calculated that air was 400 times lighter than water, it depressed the mercury more than the introduction of an equal amount of water. Noël and his pupil Descartes believed that the 'space' was not a vacuum but contained something they termed aether. They explained the puzzling difference between inserting air and water by postulating that air contained many times more aether than water. Opposing their view was Giles Personne de Roberval (1602-1675), the professor of mathematics at the College Royale in Paris, who had devised many experiments in the space above the mercury column. His introduction of measured volumes of air and water gave the same result as that of Noël. Then Roberval devised an experiment using the swim bladder of a carp as a balloon. Introduced in the space above the mercury, the collapsed bladder expanded. These experiments in Paris attracted many observers, one being Jean Pecquet (1622-1674), a physician and anatomist. Pecquet had described the thoracic duct and the lymphatic system, adding this important physiological knowledge

to Harvey's description of the circulation of the blood. Pecquet strongly
supported Harvey against his critics, notably Jean Riolan of Paris. As we shall
describe later, Power was greatly influenced by Harvey's work on the circulation
of the blood and Pecquet's description of the lymphatic system, and wrote on
both of these subjects himself.[24] [25] In our narrative, Pecquet's *Experimenta
Nova Anatomica* is important, as this book, and an English translation of it,
were in Power's library. The book described the experiment of Blaise Pascal
(1623-1662) discussed below. In Paris the mercury experiments were seen by
Pascal, who reasoned that the mercury column, being supported by air pressure,
would be lower if the experiment was conducted at a higher altitude. He had
previously observed that a half-filled balloon expanded when taken to a higher
altitude. He tested his hypothesis by successive measurements at the foot and
the top of a church steeple in Paris. His results were inconclusive, because of
the modest difference in height, and he proceeded to a historic experiment on
the Puy de Dôme, a high mountain in Auvergne, near Clermont. The experiment
was performed by Florin Perier, the brother-in-law of Pascal, on the 19th
September 1648, and was entirely successful. Two identical glass tubes 4 feet
long, each sealed at one end, were filled with mercury and inverted into a vessel
containing mercury. The level of the mercury in both was 26 inches and 3.5
lines. One tube remained at Clermont, whilst the other was carried to the top
of the Puy de Dôme, filled again with mercury and inverted as before, when the
mercury level was observed to be 23 inches and 2 lines, a diminution of 3 inches
and 1.5 lines. Meanwhile the mercury level in the tube remaining at Clermont
had not changed. Pascal wrote an account of this experiment in 1648.[26]
However, the result of this experiment was not generally known until 1651,
when Pecquet's *Experimenta nova anatomica* appeared.[27] It was reading this
work that prompted Power to confirm the experiment of Pascal in Halifax in
1653, which event preceded any successful altitude experiment by researchers
in Oxford and London. The Scot, George Sinclair, working in Glasgow, was
experimenting on the effect of altitude on a mercury column, but his work was
not published until 1669.[28]

Experiments on barometric pressure in England[29]

The Torricellian experiment and its many variations, in which the behaviour of
the contents of a vacuum were studied, became a popular study and knowledge
of this work began to spread. From France, the disseminating knowledge of the
new science came from Mersenne's circle in Paris, but the English virtuosi were
also travelling to Italy. Samuel Hartlib (c.1600–1670) was a frequent
correspondent of Mersenne. Sir Charles Cavendish (1591–1654), exiled in
Paris during the Civil War, describes the experiment in a letter to William Petty,
dated April 1648:

They prepare a long tube ... which is filled with quicksilver ... and being stopped by ones finger the tube is inverted and plunged in a vessel halfe or more filled with quicksilver. The quicksilver in ye tube will force ye quicksilver in ye vessel to rise ... and so leaves a space in ye top of the tube vacuum as is supposed[30]

This letter to William Petty brings to mind the importance of the Jesuit College, La Flèche, near Caen. Petty, by the merest chance, was educated at La Flèche, where Descartes was taught by Noël.[31] And earlier, we have described how the investigation of barometric pressure began with the work of Beeckman, whose thesis was presented to the University of Caen. In France, there are frequent reports of the 'mercury experiment' and many variations were performed in London, Cambridge and Oxford. Wherever a group of philosophers (scientists) gathered, they were fascinated by the properties of the vacuum above the mercury level. In London, there were informal meetings of which there are only fragmentary records but the attenders probably included : John Wilkins, Jonathan Goddard, George Ent, Francis Glisson, Christopher Merret, Samuel Foster, and Theodore Haak. The last mentioned, Theodore Haak, was prominent in these meetings, as he had travelled widely in Europe and was a correspondent of Mersenne, as is evident in a letter dated 24th March and 3rd April, 1648, from which this extract follows :

We have made two or three trials of it, in the company of men of letters and rank ... I shall attempt to encourage some of the best wits to make some investigation of the basis of these observations.[32]

In 1647, the Parliamentary Army occupied London, causing considerable disruption. Some philosophers moved to Oxford, which by 1648 had become an active scientific centre. Samuel Hartlib (1595/1600-1662), a friend of Haak and another correspondent of Mersenne, was important in relaying scientific news. In March 1646/1647 he was writing to Boyle :

... I read, not long since, in a late mechanical treatise of the excellent Mersennes, both the construction and use of this engine (wind gun), and amongst the uses, one, whose stratagem obliged me to take of it particular notice; and it was, how by the help of this instrument to discover the weight of the air, which, for all the prattling of our book philosophers, we must believe to be both heavy and ponderable, if we will not refuse belief to our senses.[33]

The Honourable Robert Boyle, the son of the fabulously wealthy Earl of Cork, had come to Oxford – possibly on the suggestion of William Petty – as an independent scientist. Boyle engaged Robert Hooke as his assistant in his researches, which were initially concentrated on the study of air pressure. Another correspondent with news from France was Sir Charles Cavendish (159?-1654), who had been in exile in Europe during the Civil Wars. During three years in Paris from 1645-1648 he had met Mersenne and Descartes and several of the persons mentioned above. In the Hartlib papers in the Sheffield University Library is a letter, dated April 7th/19th, from Cavendish in Paris to Petty. The following extract exemplifies the ease of transmission of scientific knowledge in the 17th century from France to England :

> There is an experiment, how to show as they suppose that there is, or may be a vacuum. It may bee it was here before you went from hence. It were too long to recite all the particulars, but in brief thus, they prepare a long tube like a weather-glasse, which is filled with quicksilver, and being stopt as close as may be with ones finger the tube is inverted and plunged into a vessell halfe or more full of quicksilver. The quicksilver in ye tube will force the quicksilver in ye vessell to rise by adding more quicksilver to it, and so leaves a space in ye top of the tube vacuum as is supposed but a bladder being hung in that vacuum, was as perfectly seene as could be, so that there must bee somebody there to convey ye Action of light to ye and you as I suppose and divers others heere, that the bladder was made as flat as they could, then they put it in, and when then quicksilver left it, it swelled in that supposed vacuum like a little football.[34]

In tracing the introduction of the 'mercury experiments' to England we come to Walter Charleton (1619-1707), a physician trained at Oxford, where he gained his degree in 1641, a generation before Power, who in that year began his studies at Cambridge. Charleton's early publications were on medical subjects but in 1654 his *Physiologica Epicuro-Gassendo-Charltoniana* shows a profound grasp of the subject of this chapter.[35] Charleton was not an experimenter but had read widely and had carefully considered the evidence of the two opposing theories of the 'plenists' and the 'vacuists', relating them to the 'Cartesians' and the 'Gassendists'. Charleton in this controversy preferred the views of Gassendi to those of Descartes. Many of his statements are taken from Gassendi, from whom his references to other works are derived. Charleton welcomed the 'mercury experiment' as an

> 'opportunity to challenge all the Wits of Europe to an aemulous combat for the honour of perspicacity' and presented 'to our judicious reader, a faithful Transcript of the Experiment, together with the most rational solutions of all admirable Appearances observed therein ... .'

This publication in 1654 probably precedes any other publication in England that describes the 'mercury experiment'. But already in 1653, Power was making his barometric experiment on Halifax Hill.

Henry Power's mercury experiments

Power's early death curtailed the publication of much of his research in other subjects but fortunately most of his mercury experiments are described in *Experimental Philosophy* (figs 5.1 & 5.2).[36] Power carefully preserved his manuscript notes and texts, most of which have come to the British Library. Of his barometric research at Cambridge and Halifax, there are three manuscript versions, two in the British Library and one in the Bodleian Library.[37] [38] The British Library *Sloane MS 1333 ff. 133-141* is the bound notebook of a military engineer, to which is appended a shortened, incomplete version in Latin of Power's barometric experiments. *Sloane MS 1393 ff. 134-153* is the version from which Power's *Experimental Philosophy* was printed (Fig. 5.3). It is in Power's hand, with minor corrections and additions, and almost every page is signed. Comparison with the book shows that further changes were made, possibly in proof. For example, Torricelli is described in the *MS* as the 'French Engineer', but becomes the 'eminent Mathematician' in the book. The Bodleian *Ashmolean MS 1400, ff. 15-21* is a copy of the original notes of the experiment made, according to a note in the *MS*, by 'John Sponge'. Mr John Spong (b. 1623) was a mathematician and instrument maker in London. The date of the Sponge manuscript – September, 1677 – demonstrates the interest in Power's work 24 years after the experiment on Halifax Hill and 13 years after its publication.

The second book of *Experimental Philosophy* is headed 'Mercurial Experiments. Begun *Anno Domini* 1653'.[39] Power wished his readers to know that the experiments were performed ten years before publication. And whilst the official publication date of the whole book is 1664, this *Liber Secundus* states : 'London, Printed in the Year 1663'. The preface is signed : 'Henry Power. From New Hall near Hallifax, 1. Aug. 1661'. This book, now in a 2009 reprint, sets out clearly most if not all of Power's mercurial experiments. We begin with 'Such things as are requisite ...' which is reproduced in Figure 5.1. Experiment 1 describes the original Torricellian experiment.[40] Power then describes fourteen 'rare observables' (Fig. 5.2). To achieve a mercury level with a space above, the glass tube has to be longer than 29 inches, which is the level he constantly attained. Greater or lesser bore diameters of the tubing did not alter the height nor did addition or subtraction of mercury from the vessel. Tilting the tube caused the mercury to pass further along the tube but did not rise above 29 inches above the level in the vessel. Heat and cold applied to the

The Second Book.

Thefe Phyſico-Mechanical Ex-⎱ *Hydrargyral,*
periments are of four ſorts, ⎰ *Hydraulical,*
⎰ *Pneumatical,* and
⎰ *Mixt.*

Such things as are requiſite for the triall of theſe Experiments, are

1. *A Quart at leaſt of* (☿) *Quickſilver.*
2. *Several Glaſs-Trunks, or Cylindrical Glaſs-Tubes, ſome
   open at both ends, and ſome exactly cloſed; or (as they
   phraſe it) Hermetically ſealed at the one end. All of ſeveral Lengths and Bores.*
3. *A Glaſs-Tunnel or two, with wooden diſhes and ſpoons, for
   filling of the Glaſs-Tubes with* Mercury.
4. *You muſt have no Metalline Utenſils about you, for fear they
   be ſpoiled with the* Mercury.
5. *Spread a Blanket or Carpet on the ground when you try theſe
   Experiments, that ſo none of the* Mercury *may be loſt,
   but may be taken up again with wooden ſpoons.*
6. *You may have by you alſo Glaſs-Syphons, Weather-Glaſſes
   of ſeveral right and crooked ſhapes,* &c. *the more to ad-
   vantage the Experiments.*

Figure 5.1 Page 88 of *Experimental Philosophy* listing requirements for the
mercury experiments.

tube caused a slight change, ascending or descending 'as the water in a Weather-
glass'. Experiment 12 involved closing the end of the tube in the vessel with
one's thumb. On removing the tube from the vessel '... your thumb will be
drawn and suck'd into the orifice of the tube, not without some considerable
pain'. Reversing the tube then causes the mercury to move swiftly towards the
sealed end, with some danger, as 'I once brake a Glass-tube near forty inches
long, by plucking it suddenly out of the vessel'd Mercury'. In Observable 18
(p.93), Power compares his mercury height of 29 inches with that observed by
'Forrain Experimenters', whose figure was usually 27 inches. He suggests
several reasons but his '... diversity of our measures and theirs ...' correctly
explained the difference. In Chapter II, Power reflects on the space above the
mercury, which he denies is 'an absolute Vacuity'. He reasons that light requires
something to be lit and that :

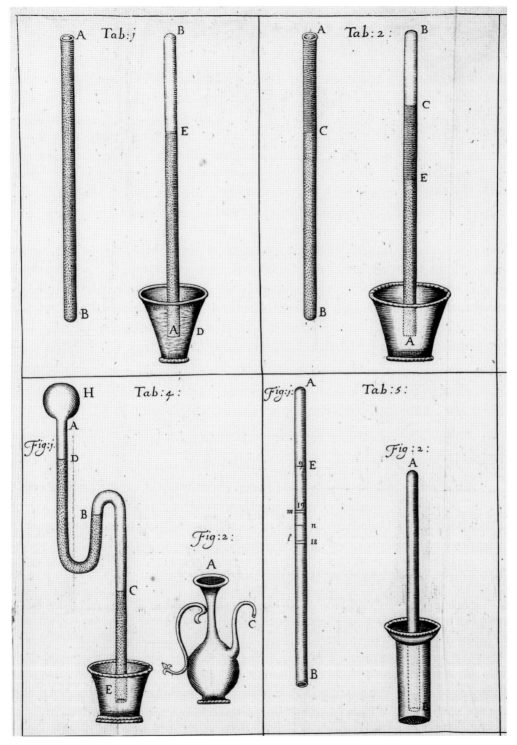

Figure 5.2 Four drawings selected from nine illustrations in *Experimental Philosophy* of various mercury experiments.

> The most full evidence against this pretended Vacuity is from the returgenscency of the empty Bladder suspended in this Vacuity ; for how should it be so fully blown from nothing ?

The swim bladder experiment was used as evidence for and against a vacuum by both 'plenists' and 'vacuists' with differing interpretations. Power now considers the alternate explanations of the 'seeming vacuity' : That it contains 'Spirits Mercurial, or Exhalations' is disproved as a similar experiment was performed by Pascal using a 46 foot lead pipe filled with water and reversed into a pail of water. Also, when Power used a 'Glass-Syringe or Squirt' under water, he did '... draw back the Squirt-staff, and the Syringe will appear a Vacuity ...' Clearly a 'Vacuity' can be produced without the presence of mercury. Power, using a four-foot gun barrel instead of a glass tube, demonstrated ingeniously that the mercury experiment could be performed without light. That the space contained little or no atmospheric air was shown by experiment 5 (p. 100) in which, after the usual preliminaries, water was added to the mercury vessel. Raising the tube so that the open end was in water caused a confusion of mercury and water, that settled into a filled tube with water above and mercury below.[41] Power concluded :

> This Truth also is manifestly evinced from the twelfth Observable annexed to the first Hydrargyral Experiment, which palpably shows that it is not common Air which supplies the seeming Vacuity.

Power follows Roberval and Pecquet (p. 101) in postulating a 'Spontaneous Eleter' made of 'particles of Ayr', which are like :

> ... many little springs, which if at liberty, and not bound and squeesed up, will powerfully, strongly, and spontaneously dilate and stretch out themselves, not onely to fill up a large room, but to remove great bodies ...

Then Power, quoting Pecquet (p. 101) :

> ... compares this vast Element of Air; circumsused about this terraqueous Globe, to a great heap of Wooll–fleeces or Sponges, piled one upon another, the superior particles of Ayr pressing the inferior ...

Now Power understands clearly that air has substance and presses down on whatever is below. And it has power which can be applied rapidly : ' ... Just like the Spring of a Watch (which if the String be broke, presently flyes out into its fullest expansion) ...' Power is recalling the sudden movement of mercury in his experiments with a force sufficient to break his glass tubes. And now comes Power's barometric experiment introduced as follows (p. 104):

I have an experiment in Banco which will give some Mechanical Evidence of this great Mystery, which here, with all its consequences, I shall deliver.

This Experiment 7 has been set in type from the text in *Sloane MS. 1393, folio 144*, reproduced in Figure 5.3 and is summarised in the first paragraph :

The 6. of May, 1653. I took two Tubes, one of 45. inches, the other 35 ½ in length, and of different Diameters ; and filling them both at the Bottom of *Hallifax–Hill*, the Quicksilver in both came down to its wonted pitch of 29 inches, thence going immediately to the top of the said Hill, and repeating the Experiment again, we found it there to fall more than half an inch lower than it did at the bottom or foot of the said Hill.

Power had now attained a complete understanding of his experiments and gave unequivocal explanations of his results (p. 105).

Why it falls no lower than 29. Because a Cylinder of that weight does just æquipose the Elastick power of the Ayr without, and therefore after a few vibrations up and down … they arrive at a Counterpoise.

The Halifax Hill experiment is clearly explained (p.105) :

… why the Counterpoise should alter at the top from that at the bottom of the Hill, and the descent of the Quicksilver be so unequal, is … from the variation of the gravity of the Superincumbent Ayr: For, a longer, and so consequently, more weighty column of Ayr, presses upon the vessel'd Quicksilver at the bottom of the Mountain, and so makes the Quicksilver in the Tube, rise higher than at the top of the Mountain ; which being so much nearer the top of the Atmosphere …

Power now makes a bold deduction and forecasts (pp. 105–6):

And if the Experiment could be try'd at the top of the Atmosphere, no Quicksilver at all would remain in the Tube, but fall down to a level with that in the vessel.

Power indicated that his barometer will function as an altimeter :

… we might … find out the Perpendicular height of our great Hill here at Hallifax, or any other Mountain whatsoever …

And finally in a suggestion that found favour with the fledgling Royal Society :

I could wish that some of our *Canary* Merchants would get this Experiment try'd at the top of the Pike of *Teneriffe*, which is deservedly famed for the highest Hill in the World.

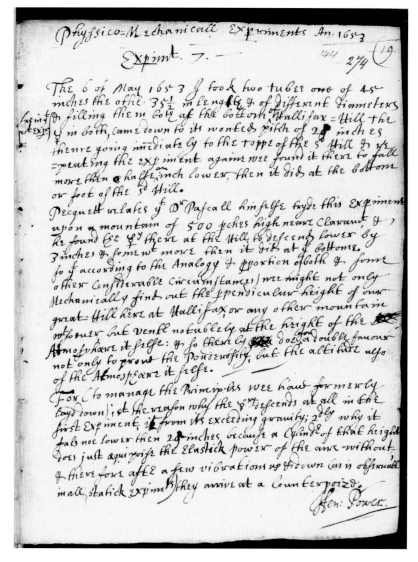

Figure 5.3 Manuscript page in the hand of Power and signed, bottom right, describing Experiment 7 on May 6th, 1653.

Henry Power and the Royal Society of London

The Royal Society was founded in 1660.[42][43] For some years, small groups of scientists – clubs of the virtuosi – had met informally in London and these meetings began to be focussed on Gresham College. The Civil Wars caused great disturbance in London, and when the Parliamentary Army occupied the City in 1647, many members of these informal groups dispersed and many left for Oxford. In 1648, William Petty had come to Oxford, first as a Fellow of Brasenose College, then its Vice-Principal, then Tomlins Reader in Anatomy and finally Professor of Public Anatomy.[44] John Wilkins had become Warden of Wadham College in April 1648, Dr Wallis was appointed to the Chair of Geometry in June 1649, Seth Ward to the Chair of Astronomy in 1649, and Dr Goddard to be Warden of Merton College in December 1651. These, with Ralph Bathurst, Robert Wood and Thomas Willis met first in Petty's lodgings in the High and, after Petty's departure to Ireland in December, 1652, in Dr Wilkin's apartments in Wadham College. This concentration of scientists in Oxford included many who later formed the Royal Society of London, founded by the restored Charles II.

It was inevitable that an experimenter such as Power would be attracted to the Society and that its members would wish to be informed of his researches. An old friend of Power living in Maldon was Matthew Robinson (1628-1694), a fellow of Christ's College, Cambridge.[45] In April 1661, Power enquired of Robinson about the new College.[46] Contact with the College was made through John Tillotson (1630-1694), a boyhood friend of Power and a future Archbishop of Canterbury. Tillotson described Power and his experiments to the Registrar of the Society and, on the 8th of May, the members agreed on his admission.[47] The Registrar wrote to Power for details of his experiments[48], and Power replied by 'sending a book on mercuriall experiments'[49], which was examined by the Society in October.[50] These reports so interested the Society that they requested Power to extend his observations[51] and Power was elected a member on the 26th of February, 1662.[52] [53] Then followed a period of extensive correspondence between Power and the Society. He was asked to observe the weather in Halifax[54] and a thermometer was sent to him.[55] He reported on 'tampering with the load-stone'[56] and on experiments on gravity.[57] He was asked to measure temperatures in caves[58] and make further experiments underground.[59] Robert Hooke, now the Curator of the Society, was requested to verify these experiments underground.[60] Power was asked to observe a lunar eclipse at Halifax in February, 1663[61] and a comet.[62] Power reported to the Society his instrument to 'demonstrate the Copernican theory'.[63] His correspondence with the Society continued. He was asked for the writings of amateur astronomers in his neighbourhood[64] and was also asked to make further experiments underground.[65] Power's experimental work was exactly that which interested these early scientists. But as a physician with a medical practice in Halifax, he could scarcely attend even a few of the weekly meetings in London and he could only figure as a correspondent from Yorkshire. Scientists such as Robert Boyle and Robert Hooke and many others were permanently in London and became central figures in the Society. Power's scientific interests had waned but were aroused by a new friend, Richard Towneley, of a prominent Lancashire family.

The Towneley Family

This family had been settled at Towneley, near Burnley in Lancashire since the early 13th century.[66] They were descended from Geoffrey, the Dean of Whalley Abbey, and, subsequent to the dissolution of the monasteries in the 16th century, had acquired extensive estates, particularly around Burnley in Lancashire but also in Lincolnshire and Nottinghamshire. Their country seats were Towneley Hall (Figs. 5.4 & 5.5) in Lancashire and Nocton Abbey in Lincolnshire. The history of this family is long and complex but may be summarised as a wealthy Catholic family who survived many political storms mainly caused by their staunch adherence to their chosen religious faith. The 17th century Civil Wars were disastrous, as both Charles and Christopher fought for the King in the Lancashire army which they helped to raise. Towneley Hall fell to the Parliamentarians at the beginning of the war, and the two brothers crossed the Pennines to join Prince Rupert's army. At the battle of Marston Moor in 1644, Charles was killed and Christopher was captured. It is a measure of the resilience of the family, that they eventually regained Towneley Hall, although they lost several of their other estates. Richard, who concerns us here, was the eldest son of Charles Towneley's seven children. As was the case with most wealthy Catholic families he was privately educated by a family tutor and subsequently at a Catholic College on the Continent, receiving an excellent education in the classics but also in the new science of Gassendi and

Figure 5.4 Towneley Hall as it appears today.

Figure 5.5 Interior of Towneley Hall.

Descartes. We know that his younger brothers, Charles and John, were educated at Douai College. The family always maintained a comprehensive library, the contents of which are recorded. The catalogue of the library compiled *circa* 1700 is preserved in the John Rylands Library in Manchester.[67] The sale of the books of the library on the 18th of June, 1883 is known from a sale catalogue.[68] The manuscripts were sold on the 27th of June, 1883 for £4,054.[69] One of Richard's manuscripts is held by the Yale University Library.[70]

Richard Towneley and the Towneley Group

The publication in 1660 of Robert Boyle's *New Experiments Physico-Mechanical Touching the Air*[71] stimulated Power to publish – in *Experimental Philosophy* – his own findings on air pressure and to perform new experiments now in collaboration with Richard Towneley (1629-1707).[72] Towneley Hall (Figs. 5.4 & 5.5)[73] was not far from Halifax and members of the family were sometimes patients of Power.[74] These experiments were made in 1660 and 1661, and probably completed by April, 1661. Unfortunately Richard Towneley never himself published these extensive experiments but it is evident from letters to and from W. Croone and Power[75] [76] that the manuscripts of their researches were available to interested persons, of which the most important proved to be Robert Boyle. In Chapter VIII (p.121), Power emphasised that the new experiments were made at Towneley Hall, and that he had the assistance of what I term the Towneley Group.

Power's Additional Experiments

Chapter VIII is headed :

> Additional Experiments made at Townley Hall, in the years 1660 and 1661 by the advice and assistance of that Heroic and Worthy Gentleman, Richard Townley, Esq. and those Ingenious Gentlemen, Mr John, and Mr. Charles Townley, and Mr George Kemp.

Chapter VIII is introduced by a praise of Boyle's 1660 'Tractate of Experiments with his Pneumatical Engine, or Ayr-pump' and :

> I no sooner read it, but it rubbed up all my old dormant Notions, and gave me a fresh view of all my former, and almost forgotten, *Mercurial* Experiments. Nay, it had not that effect only on me, but likewise it excited and stirr'd up the noble Soul of my ever honoured friend, Mr *Townley*, together with me, to attempt these following Experiments.

Experiments 1 & 2 compared the specific gravity of mercury and water, finding that mercury was 14 times heavier than an equal volume of water. Experiment 3 used a mercury column as a barometer, observing the mercury height from the 15th of March to the 20th of April and finding a variation – up or down – of half an inch 'according to the variation of the Atmosphere'. Experiments 4-8 performed either with a siphon, glass tube, or a 'glass-Cruet' examined the admixture of air, water, oil, and milk on the mercury column. Experiment 6, introducing air, will be mentioned below. Experiment 9 (pp. 126-7) was performed on the 27th of April, 1661, when the mercury level was measured 'in the Porch at the new Church in Pendle' and found to be 28 ¼ inches. At the Beacon at the top of Pendle Hill the mercury height was 27 ¼ inches. At Barlow (lower than Pendle Church) the height was 28 ¼ inches.

Experiments 10 & 11 are crucial in demonstrating Boyle's Law. We have described how the experiments on Halifax Hill on the 6th of May, 1653 and on Pendle Hill on the 27th of April have shown that the mercury column varies with height. And earlier Power had tried the effect of allowing air to mix above the mercury column, which experiment was repeated with Towneley. Now these experiments 10 &11 (pp. 127-30), also on the 27th of April, combine two experiments. Air is admitted above the mercury column and by making successive measurements at the top of Pendle Hill (1800 feet) and at Barlow (800 feet) the effect of air pressure on air volume is measured. Two experiments were made, one with a glass tube of 42 inches and another with a glass tube of 26 inches. The mercury level (without any admitted air) was also measured – this was the barometric pressure – at both places. These results were tabulated :

	In the	Long Tube	
At the top	of the Hill	At the bottom of it	at Barlow
A E	50/15	50/15	} Equal parts
A D	84/75	83/8	} of Spaces,
B D	11/26	11/78	} Inches.
	In the	Lesser Tube	
At the top of	At Barlow with	At Barlow with	
the Hill	Ayr	Valley–Ayr	
A E 9	9	9	
A D 17/8	17/35	17/58	
B D 13/86	14/31	14/02	

Key: AE Ayr left in tube
       AD The ayr dilated
       BD : Quicksilver

Power concluded from the results of experiment 11 that :

> So that here is now four Proportionals, and by any three given, you may strike out the fourth, by Conversion, Transposition, and Division of them. So that by these Analogies you may prognosticate the effects, which follow in all *Mercurial* Experiments, and predemonstrate them, by calculation, before the senses give an Experimental thereof.

This appears to state that if you arrive at four proportionals [figures] such as pressure (p) 1, volume (v) 1 and pressure (p) 2 and volume (v) 2 , and if one of these is unknown, it may be calculated. p1v1 = p2v2. Boyle's Law is expressed as pv = K (when K is a constant) A difficulty in examining these results in that, whilst the barometric pressure is given in inches, the height of the mercury in the two tubes containing air is given in units or 'divisions'. The long tube of 42 inches was divided into 120 equal 'divisions' and the shorter tube of 26 inches into 31 equal 'divisions'. Whilst it might be possible to convert the divisions into inches, it is easier to convert the barometric pressure into 'divisions'.

In experiments 9 and 10 the same tube was used. This conversion has given the following figures :[77]

Locality	Barometric Height	Pressure (p)	Volume of Air (v)	Constant pv = k
Experiment 1				
Pendle Hill 1,800 feet	66.58	55.32	84.75	4,687.4
Barlow 800 feet	69.01	57.23	83.80	4,795.9
Experiment 2				
Pendle Hill	32.66	18.80	17.80	334.64
Barlow	33.86	19.49	17.35	337.63
Barlow	33.86	19.66	17.58	345.63

Power, Towneley, and Boyle

Robert Boyle is familiar to the scientific world from his Law : that the volume of a quantity of enclosed air is related directly to its pressure. Whilst the term Boyle's Law is used in the United Kingdom and North America, *La loi de Marriotte* in France claims priority of discovery for Edmé Marriotte. Marriotte's publication in 1676 follows that of Boyle by several years and his account follows closely that of Boyle.[78] Any claim of priority for Marriotte may be easily discarded. We have described above how Power and Towneley in 'Additional Experiments' arrived at the relation between the volume and pressure of air. This account was probably published in 1661 but no copy of this book has been found. Its contents are known from Power's manuscripts and were published as Book 2 of *Experimental Philosophy* in 1664 [1663]. There is ample evidence that manuscript copies of this work were sent to members of the Royal Society through Croone.[79] Boyle's publication of the second (1662) edition of his *New Experiments Physico–Mechanical Touching the Air* contains his description. This appears inconspicuously in chapters 4 & 5 of part 2 of the appendix as this second edition was issued to refute the arguments of Linus who disbelieved that the mercury column was supported by the pressure of air. Between the first edition in 1660 and the second in 1662, Boyle had seen the results of Power and Towneley, and in this second edition Boyle makes gracious acknowledgement to :

That ingenious Gentleman Mr Richard Towneley ... had endeavoured ... to supply what I had omitted concerning the reducing to a precise estimate how much Air dilated of it self loses of its Elastical force, according to the measures of its dilatation.

Boyle referred to 'Mr Towneley's hypothesis' presumably overlooking Power's part in the experiments. We conclude that Power and Towneley provided both experimental results and their interpretation, which guided Boyle to his experiments and conclusions, which have become accepted as Boyle's Law.

NOTES AND REFERENCES

1   Waard, C, de. *Correspondence de P. Marin Mersenne, religieux minime.* Volumes 1-17, Paris.
2   Waard, C. de. *L'expérience barometrique, ses antecedents et ses explications, Etude historique.* Thours, 1936.
3   Middleton, W.E.K. 'The Place of Torricelli in the History of the Barometer', *Isis,* 54 (1963), pp. 11-28.
4   Webster, C. 'The Discovery of Boyle's Law, and the Concept of the Elasticity of Air in the Seventeenth Century', *Archive for the History of Exact Sciences,* 2, pp. 441-502, 1965.
5   Webster, 1965, pp. 442-444.
6   Gallileo, G. *Le Opera*, Florence, 1894, IV, p. 167.
7   Beeckman came from the Low Countries : from what is now Belgium and Holland.
8   Beeckmann, I. MD thesis, University of Caen. An incomplete copy survives in the British Library, *BL. 1179. D.9 (3).*
9   *Journal tenu par lui de1604 à 1634, publié avec une introduction et des notes par Cornelius de Waard,* 4 volumes. La Haye, 1939–1953. The quotation is from volume 1, p. 36.
10 Waard, Mersenne, 2, pp. 282-283.
11 Rey, J. *Essays sur la recherche de la cause pour laquelle l'estain et le plomb augmentent de poids quand on les calcine,* Bazas,1630.
12 Galileo, G. *Le Opera*, XIV, 1904, pp. 127-130.
13 Galileo, G. *Dialogues concerning two new sciences.* English translation of the 1638 text by H. Crew and A. de Salvio. London and New York : 1914. Reprint New York : 1954.
14 The correspondence appears in *Le Opera*, XIV, 1904, pp. 124-125 and p. 159.
15 Maignan, E. *Cursus philosophicus concinnatus ex notissimus cuique principis.* Toulouse, 1653. The four volumes are paged as one, pp. 1925–1936.

[16] In the Vienna *Nationalbibliothek MS. 7049, letter CXXVII*. The Italian text is given in de Waard, pp. 178-181.

[17] de Waard, *L'expérience barometrique*, p. 180.

[18] Middleton, *Isis*, pp. 11-28.

[19] The page of Galileo's manuscript is reproduced in Knowles Middleton, p.18.

[20] Middleton, *Isis*, p. 19.

[21] Torricelli's two letters to Ricci are reproduced (in translation) in Knowles Middleton, pp. 19–24.

[22] Middleton, *Isis*, p. 27.

[23] De Waard, *L'Expérience barometrique*, p. 119.

[24] Power, H. *Circulation sanguinis inventio Harveiana*, British Library, *Sloane MS 1343, ff. 3-40*.

[25] Power, H. *Inventio Aselliana de Venis Lacteis et de Motu Chyli*, British Library, *Sloane MS, 1343, ff. 41-56*.

[26] Appears in *Oeuvres de Blaise Pascal*, ed. L.Brunschvicg and P. Boutroux, Paris : 1908, 2, pp. 365-373.

[27] Pecquet, J. *Experimenta nova anatomica*, Paris : 1651.

[28] Sinclari, G. *Ars Nova et Magna Gravitas et Levitas*, Roterodami, 1669, *Dialogus Primus*, pp. 125-149.

[29] Webster, C. 'The discovery of Boyle's Law, and the Concept of the Elasticity of Air on the Seventeenth Century', *Archive for the History of Exact Sciences*, vol. 2 (1965), pp. 441-502.

[30] Sheffield University Library, *Hartlib papers Bundle VII, no 29*. The letter is reproduced in Webster, 1965, p. 456.

[31] Hughes, J.T. 'William Petty : Oxford Anatomist and Physician', *Journal of Medical Biography*, 7 (1999), pp. 1-16.

[32] Letter from Theodore Haak to Mersenne dated 24th March/ 3rd April, 1648. In Harcourt Brown, *Scientific Organisations in seventeenth century France, 1620–1680*, Baltimore, 1934, p. 58.

[33] Letter from Samuel Hartlib to Boyle, 19th March, 1646/1647. In Boyle, R. *The Works of the Honourable Robert Boyle*, edited by T. Birch, 1744, vol. 1, p. 22.

[34] This letter is in the *Hartlib Papers*, Sheffield University Library. *Bundle VII, no. 29*. Reproduced in Webster, 1965, p. 450.

[35] Charleton, W. *Physiologica Epicuro-Gassendo-Charltioniana : or, a Fabrick of Science Natural, Upon the Hypothesis of Atoms*, London, 1654.

[36] Power, H. *Experimental Philosophy*, London, Printed by T. Roycroft for John Martin and James Allestry, 1664. Reprint, Oxford Rimes House, 2009 (henceforth : *Power's EP*) .

[37] British Library, Sloane *MS, 1333 ff. 133-141*, and *Sloane MS. 1393, ff. 134-153*.

38 Bodleian Library, *Ashmolean MS. 1400, ff. 15-21.*

39 *Power's EP*, pp. 85-149.

40 *Power's EP*, pp. 89-94.

41 A small bubble of air, which appeared at the top of the tube, was considered to have been introduced in error at the beginning of the experiment.

42 Birch, T. *History of the Royal Society of London*, 4 volumes. London, A Millar, 1756-1757.

43 *The Record of the Royal Society*, 3rd edition, London, Published by the Society, 1912, chapter 1.

44 Hughes, J.T. 'William Petty : Oxford Anatomist and Physician'. *Journal of Medical Biography*, 7, 1999, 1-16.

45 Power, H. Letter to Robinson from Power in Halifax dated 2nd August, BL, *Sloane MS 1326*, f. 13 r. Power was writing to Robinson about plants.

46 *Ibid, 1326 f. 20 r.*

47 Birch, VI, p. 22.

48 *Sloane, MS 1326, f. 26 v.*

49 *Ibid, f. 25 r.*

50 Birch, p. 50.

51 *Ibid*, p. 53.

52 *Ibid*, p. 27.

53 In the old Dictionary of National Biography, Power and Sir Justinian Isham are described as the first elected fellows, on the 1st of July, 1663. The confusion arises because a second royal Charter was granted to the Society in April, 1663. Although in May it had been decided that former fellows would retain their status, Power was proposed again and on the 1st of July he was again elected and formally admitted in person, *Ibid,* p. 265 and 268.

54 *Ibid*, p. 68.

55 *Ibid*, p. 320.

56 *Ibid*, p. 81.

57 Gunther, R.T. *Early Science in Oxford.* Volume 6, 1930, p. 89.

58 Birch, p. 86.

59 *Ibid*, p. 136-137, and 144.

60 *Ibid*, p. 234.

61 *Ibid*, p. 193.

62 Birch, v. 2, p. 7.

63 Ibid, p. 330.

64 *Ibid*, p. 395 and 402.

65 *Ibid*, 430 and 441. Also Gunther, p. 200.

66 Webster, C. 'Richard Towneley (1629-1707), The Towneley Group and Seventeenth Century Science'. *Transactions of the Historic Society of Lancashire and Cheshire*, 118 (1966), pp. 51-76.

[67] Towneley, R. Library Catalogue, John Rylands Library, University of Manchester, R. 72649.

[68] Towneley J. *Bibliotheca Townelsiana, 2 parts, 1814-1815. Catalogue of the Towneley library*, sold on the 18th of June, 1883. London, Sotheby, Wilkinson, and Hodge, 1883.

[69] Towneley, J. Catalogue of the Towneley Manuscripts, sold on 27th June, 1883, London, Sotheby,Wilkinson and Hodge, 1883.

[70] Towneley, R. 'Some short considerations upon Mr. Hooke's attempt for the Explication of the Expt. of waters ascent into small glass Canes', 1665-1667, Yale University Library.

[71] Boyle, R. *New Experiments Physico-Mechanical Touching the Air*, Oxford, 1650. The data and argument of what was subsequently termed Boyle's Law appeared in the second (1662) edition.

[72] Whilst the spelling, Townley, was used by Power, I have used the modern Towneley.

[73] 'Towneley Old Hall, near Burnley, Lancashire' was the subject of an article in the August 16th 1913 issue of *Country Life*, pp. 228-234.

[74] Hughes, J.T. *Dr Henry Power (1626–1668) : The Medical Practice of a Halifax Physician*, Transactions of the Halifax Antiquarian Society, 11, (2003),56-67.

[75] Croone, W. Letters to Power in the British Library, (1) September 14th, 1661, *Sloane MSS. 1326, f. 25* ; (2) January 9th, 1661, *Sloane MSS. 1326. ff. 28-29*; (3) July 20th, 1661, *Sloane MSS. 1326 f. 26.*

[76] Power, H. Letter to W. Croone in the British Library, November 27th, 1661, *Sloane MSS. 1326, f. 28.*

[77] This table is taken from Webster , 1963. p. 227.

[78] Tait, P.G. *Properties of Matter*, Edinburgh, 1885 and *Proceedings of the Royal Society of Edinburgh*, 13, p. 72, 1885

[79] See references above to correspondence between Power and Croone.

Chapter 6

The Medical Practice of a 17th Century Physician

Sacred to the memory of Henry Power, Doctor of Medicine, whose loss is universally regretted, who had a clear head, a sound judgement, together with all the accomplishments of a good Christian and a fine gentleman. And, had he lived longer, those great masters Hippocrates and Aesculapius might not only have been his pupils in their own profession, but in most other branches of polite and useful learning.

The text above translates part of the Latin on a brass plate in the floor of the middle chancel near the altar of the church of All Saints, Wakefield, where Henry Power was buried on December 23rd 1668.[1][2] Clearly Power was greatly respected locally in Halifax and Wakefield both for his medicine and for his science. This chapter describes his medical practice, almost entirely from New Hall, Elland, Halifax. Power began his medical practice in Halifax *circa* 1652, but already in 1649 he was writing from Halifax to Dr Browne '... to give me some Practicall method of the cure of some common diseases ...'[3] Strictly, he required his Cambridge MD, which was conferred in 1655, but regulations, preventing his medical practice in London or Cambridge, would not be enforced in his home town. Many other activities occupied his time: he was interested in botany and zoology and busy with his scientific work on barometric pressure. The financial accounts of his practice in Halifax are set out in detail in his papers in the British Library.[4]

The Memorandum Books

These are seven duodecimo leather bound books, the pages filled on both sides with small, moderately legible writing, mostly in the hand of Henry Power, whose elaborate signature often appears. When an account had been paid, the writing is heavily crossed out, adding to difficulty in decipherment. My reference gives the number of pages in each book. The sides, *recto* and *verso*, number 1472. From such extensive accounts, only a selection can be made here, in which previous work on these books by J.W. Clay is invaluable.[5] The accounts give details of a thriving medical practice in Halifax and beyond, the families mentioned including gentry in the neighbourhood, and many at a distance. As a physician, Power had no rival for his services. Raach compiled a directory of English Country Physicians from 1603-1643 (the period before Power commenced his practice) and made no entry for Halifax.[6] Sam Midgely, writing in 1708, describes the Halifax physicians in the seventeenth century as

Drs Power, Wilkinson, Maud, and Threadland.[7] None of these names appear in the Munk's Roll of the Royal College of Physicians of London. The last three mentioned have left little mark. Anthony Wood wrote that a Jonathan Maud of Halifax was created MD in June, 1652, because ' ... he hath been a constant friend to the parliament ... '.[8] It is probable that any practice of Maud was confined to London.

Power's patients

In the following extracts, the principal families are noted and the individuals mentioned were patients.

ARMYTAGE: Sir John Armytage, of Kirlees. Widow Armytage and daughter, of Kerresforth Hill. CLAY: John Clay and family, of Clay House, Greetland, and Gilbert Clay, of Elland. CONYERS: Mrs Conyers, of Farnley Hall. COPLEY: Edward Copley, of Batley. FARRAR: John Farrar and his son, Brearley, of Ewood. FOXCROFT: Prominent and numerous, the Foxcrofts were related to the doctor in two ways. His widowed mother had married Anthony Foxcroft, the daughter of whom Henry had married. Patients were Sam Foxcroft of Kebroyd, and 'Squire' James and Grace Foxcroft. HORN: Mr Horn, of Almondbury. HORTON: William (Squire). JACKSON: Lady Jackson,

Figure 6.1 Woodhouse, Rastrick from a lithograph by John Horner. This was the residence of Squire Richard and Mary Law, patients of Power.

Figure 6.2 Lithograph by John Horner, dated 1835, of Shibden Hall,
as viewed from Beacon Hill. This was the main residence of the Lister family of
Mr & Mrs Thomas Lister, patients of Power.

of Hutton-Pannal. KAYE: Sir John Kaye, of Woodsome. LAW: Richard (Squire) and Mary Law, of Woodhouse, Rastrick (Fig. 6.1). LINLEY: Mr Linley, of Almonbury. LISTER: The main residence of the Listers was Shibden Hall (Fig. 6.2), where Mr and Mrs Thomas Lister were patients, as were members of other branches. Mr John Lister, of Ovenden, was cousin to Thomas. Mr John Lister, of Bawtry, was of an older branch which had settled near Hull, and visited by Power from Wakefield. RAMSDEN: John and Richard Ramsden, of Rastrick and Robert Ramsden, of Stonyroyd, were patients close at hand, but distant were William and Elizabeth Ramsden, of Longley, near Huddersfield. SAVILLE: Mrs Saville, of Copley. WATERHOUSE: Isaac Waterhouse, of Elland. Arthur Waterhouse, of Birstall. WENTWORTH: Ann Wentworth, of Woodsome. WHITTEL: John Whittel, of Whittel Place, Elland.

To the list above we may add other place names distant from Halifax and mentioned in his practice: Almondbury, Batley, Barnsley (Kerresforth Hill), Bierley, Bingley, Birstall, Bolton-by-Bolland, Bowling, Bradford, Burnley (Towneley Hall), Cawthorn, Crofton, Dewsbury, Farnley, Hopton, Horbury, Horsforth, Huddersfield, Huntroid, Kirkheaton, Leeds, Middleton, Milnthorpe, Normanton, Okenshaw, Pomfret, Skiers, Wakefield, Welbeck, Wentworth.

Diagnoses and Therapies

Whilst other expenses also appear, accounts generally record fees charged, often stating the medicine supplied or the service given. Diagnoses are less confident, reflecting the state of medicine in the mid-seventeenth century, but some are recognisable. Cerebral vascular stroke causing a hemiplegia appears under several names. Colic is common and sometimes can be assigned to the urinary system. Gouty joints in the toes are described, and scabies appears several times. The diagnosis of scurvy was made frequently, and used for several states, not necessarily avitaminosis C. Fevers were common and intermittent fever was distinguished. But many 'diagnoses' are descriptive of localised pain, or more generalised discomfort, and include melancholy and hysteria.

A common prescription was a 'diet bag' in which medicinal herbs were contained in two gallons of ale or wine. The price was often 4s 6d, but sometimes more. Nathaniel Tilson's 'wife's nurses kins-woman' was charged 5s 6d for a diet bag of 8 or 9 quarts of Rhenish wine. Sir John Armytage was charged 11s, but prescriptions to the titled appear to have cost more than those to the gentry. A pint of carminative water cost Sir John 5s 6d, whilst a pint of the best cinnamon water cost 6s 6d. 'Clysters', which were enemas, cost about 3s 6d, whilst a 'glyster bagge', to contain the fluid, added 3d. An 'Electuary' consisted of powdered drugs in a syrup, usually made from honey, and might cost 4s. Similar were 'cordials' and 'Julaps'. Drugs were prescribed as draughts, powders, pills, or lozenges. Purgatives were common, as an electuary, or a powder, and might cost 1s. Some patients were nobility. 'My Lady Saville', 27 years of age and suffering from melancholy, was charged 12s 6d for a 'box of best Pascalian lozenges, gilt with silver and gold interchangeably', and the 'old' Countess of Sussex at Howley Hall, was prescribed a 'black electuary' and a 'white electuary', whilst the 'young' Countess received a 'large pint liquid cordial', costing 8s 6d.

Medicine was frequently sent, particularly for repeat prescriptions, which were common. Power charged from 20s to 40s for a consultation, not excessive, considering the distance to some of his patients. He journeyed to his patients on horseback, as the hills around Halifax, and the wretched roads did not suit a carriage and coachman, for which there is no evidence in the accounts.[9] We read that, in 1655, he sold his 'sorrel mare' to Capt. Edward Ward for £ 5.

Power's extensive library included most of the common medical textbooks, including ancient and modern texts (Figure 4).[10] Aristotle and Galen (in two vols.) contrasted with Paracelsus (in four vols.), Harvey, Browne, Willis, and Highmore. Power tried to identify specific diseases, a modern approach assuming that diseases have different causes, and rejecting the old concept, from Hippocrates and Galen, of humours and imbalances of the body.[11] This belief had considered the four elements, earth, water, fire, and air, were related to four body humours, blood, phlegm, yellow bile, and black bile. Restoring the balance of the humours was the aim of treatment of an illness, and the actions of drugs were classified as simples, compounds, or entities. Simples, made from one species of herb, affected one humour. Compounds, made from two or more herbs, had a main effect and a second effect. Entities were 'efficient' drugs, which included purgatives, emetics, poisons, and antidotes. They had one specific effect but on the whole body. Powerful emetics and purges were favoured and, also, bleeding and blistering, the use of which persisted for many years, being cruelly applied to Charles II, accelerating his death in 1685. Power did not use bleeding or blistering, nor did he prescribe emetics, and his purgatives were probably mild laxatives. He was interested in chemistry and might have taken up the ideas of the Paracelsians, had these been more accessible to him.[12] His therapies were medicinal herbs, which he grew in his garden, gathered in the fields, or procured from suppliers. His library had many herbal textbooks.

Plague at Wakefield

We have described earlier that in 1664, Power moved to Wakefield.[13]

His Memorandum Book notes his move: '… that I came to Wakefield to live 7 of October 1664 wch was on a Friday.'[14] After this date, the entries of visits, prescriptions, and fees continue but are more directed to patients around Wakefield.

The Great Plague visited London in 1665, but there were outbreaks in many other towns throughout the country and, as a proportion of the population affected, the inhabitants of some towns and villages suffered more than those in London. Outbreaks of plague had recurred throughout the country for centuries and were common in Yorkshire towns, as is evident from burial records, which often state the presumed cause of death. The parish records of Wakefield and Leeds record an outbreak beginning in 1625. From the 7th of August, 1625 to the 15th of January, 1626, the parish register of Wakefield Church attributed 131 deaths to the plague out of a total of 205 deaths.[15] Another epidemic occurred in 1645, the year after Power moved to Wakefield when, out of 407 deaths, 245 were caused by plague. In this year 1325 died of plague in Leeds.[16] The appearance of cases of plague in a town was a dreadful visitation. The cause was not understood and, as many cases were fatal irrespective of treatment, measures were more concerned with the avoidance of infection. Physicians often did not visit cases. In London, the response of the Fellows of the Royal College of Physicians in 1665 was to leave the city.

The civic authorities in London and elsewhere had obligations from the Act of 1604, renewed in 1628.[17] If a stricken town could not provide for itself, neighbouring towns were obliged to assist. When Dewsbury experienced a serious epidemic, the Justices at Wakefield were informed in January, 1641 that :

> ... it hath pleased God to visit the inhabitants of Dewsbury for several months with a heavy visitation and that Trade and Commerce had so much decayed and the poor so increased that about 270 and odd persons had to receive weekly allowance and relief.[18]

The Constables of a town had wide powers to prevent the spread of infection. Keepers of alehouses were forbidden to sell ale and beer to strangers with especial prohibition if persons had come from a town with plague. When, in 1665, the plague in London caused many to flee the city, the inhabitants of Yorkshire feared the import of the infection. Wakefield, in some measure the gateway from the South, was considered to be vulnerable, and its bailiff and constables were ordered to :

> Keep all carriers and commodities they bring from London, and all other passengers which tradeth which may be suspected to be dangerous, and to examine their passes and to use their utmost care and diligence in everything as they will answer for their negligence and contempt therein.[19]

Constables could take action against any houses that sheltered visitors from London. A watch would be posted on such a house, which might be locked for some weeks to the distress of the inhabitants and the owner of the house who was required to pay the costs of the surveillance. These measures taken by the constables of the town were of some assistance in limiting the spread of cases. Physicians were inactive and impotent during an epidemic of plague and there is no record that Power was engaged in treating cases of the plague. His medical practice diminished after his move to Wakefield and, as described in chapter 4, he died in 1668 and was buried on December 23rd in the Parish Church.

NOTES AND REFERENCES

1   Thomas Gent of York, *The Ancient and Modern History of the Loyal Town of Rippon*, (York, 1763), pp. 13-14.
2   Sisson, J.L. *Historic Sketch of the Parish Church, Wakefield*, Wakefield, 1824, pp. 40-41.
3   Letter to Browne, August 28th, 1649, *MS. Sloane 1911-1913, f. 82.* Reproduced in Keynes, 6, pp. 287-288.
4   British Library, *Memorandum Books, 7 vols. Sloane MSS.1351, 1353-1358.*

5 Clay, J.W. 'Dr. Henry Power of New Hall, F.R.S.' *Papers, Reports etc. read to (later Transactions of) the Halifax Antiquarian Society*, 1917, pp. 1-31.

6 J.H. Raach, *A Directory of English Country Physicians 1603-1643*, (London, 1962), pp. 119-128.

7 S. Midgely. *Halifax and its Gibbet-Law Placed in a True Light*, printed by J. How for William Bentley (Halifax, 1708).

8 Anthony A Wood, *Athenae Oxoniensis & The Fasti*, ed. P Bliss, (London, 1820), vol. 4, p. 173.

9 Goods were transported by pack animals traversing a narrow paved path called a 'causey'. C. Clegg, 'Coaching Days', *THAS*, (1923), 123-158.

10 'A catalogue of all my Books taken the 1st of September 1664 just before my removall to Wakefield', *Sloane MS. 1346*.

11 O. Temkin, *Galenism: Rise and Decline of a Medical Philosophy*, (Ithaca and London, 1973), p. 103.

12 See A.G. Debus, *The English Paracelsians*, (New York, 1966).

13 Clay, p. 6.

14 *Sloane, MS 1358 f.1.*

15 Walker, J.W. *History of Wakefield Parish Church*, Wakefield, Published by the Author, 1966, p. 306.

16 Whittaker, T. *Loidis et Elmete*, 1816, p. 76.

17 *2 James I. c. 31 and Charles I. c. 4.*

18 *QSR Order Book, A ff. 145 and 146. Wakefield, Jan. 1640/1*. In Waters, S.H. *Wakefield in the Seventeenth Century*, Wakefield, Sanderson & Clayton, 1933, p. 139-140.

19 *QSR . Order Book. G. f. 13*. In Waters, p. 142.

Chapter 7

Power and William Harvey's *De Motu Cordis*

There has not one Day pass'd, since that worthy production of his was first deliver'd into the world, but it hath mett with men of sevral humours and constitutions, some with very smart and active Discourse maintaining and avouching it, others with as much vehemency and passion busily refuting it ... Amongst all the rabble of his antagonists, we see not one that attempts to fight him at his own weapon, that is by sensible and Anatomical evictions to Confute that, which he has by Sense and Autopsy so vigourously Confirm'd.[1]

The quotation above is from Power's extensive notes under the heading *Circulatio Sanguinis, Inventio Harveiana*, dated 1652. On 15 September 1648 Power, writing to Browne, reports that he had :

... run through the whole body of Anatomy Insisting on Spigelius, Bartholinus, Fernelius, Columbus, Veslingius, but especially Harvey's Circulation, & the two Incomparable Authors, DesCartes, & Regius ...[2]

Power, more than Browne, looked to recent and contemporary authors for guidance in science and medicine. He also extended and replicated observations and experiments, as in his work on the mercury barometer in 1653.[3] In anatomy, a year earlier, after studying the writings of Harvey on the circulation of the blood, he began a series of observations and experiments to confirm Harvey's work. In 1652 Power commenced his medical practice in Halifax, where his anatomical work, begun in Cambridge, was completed.[4]

Harvey and De Motu Cordis

The publication in 1628 by William Harvey (1578-1657) (Figs. 7.1, 7.2 & 7.3) of his study of the circulation of the blood is a milestone in anatomy, physiology and medicine, possibly the greatest in the history of these subjects.[5] This was celebrated 300 years later.[6] There have been several modern translations.[7] These have been listed and discussed by K.J. Franklin.[8] The content of this book marks the transition between medicine and science based mainly on Aristotle and Galen, and modern observations and research, which today continue the work and teaching of Harvey, whose life has attracted many biographers.[9]

The profound change in thinking after 1628 is evident by comparing it with the writings of Galen on the functions of the organs of body.[10] Galen viewed the organs as a system in which nutrients were assimilated and the life force created. The food, after digestion in the stomach, became chyle, which passed through the portal vein into the liver to form blood. The blood entered the *vena cavae* and was distributed throughout the body by the veins. Part went to the right ventricle of the heart and, through the pulmonary arteries, nourished the lungs and was purified by the air. Some of the blood in the right ventricle went though pores into the left ventricle, and received air, or pneuma, from the trachea *via* the pulmonary vein. This air, containing vital spirit, acted on the blood in the left ventricle to form arterial blood, which passed with air into the aorta and all the arteries, including those to the brain.[11] There was an idea of ebb and flow of blood, but it was thought that most of the blood created in the liver was consumed in the tissues throughout the body. Galen's teaching of anatomy and physiology dominated understanding of disease, and prejudiced therapy, an example being the practice of bleeding to correct imbalance of body humours, when the side and place whence blood was removed were all important. Galen's teaching, inconsistent with modern anatomy and physiology, was the basis of medicine in Europe and the Arab world for over 1500 years.[12] There is a paradox in this enthusiasm for Aristotle and Galen. Medical teaching in Greek and Latin was largely lost in Europe – but not in the Arab world – during the dark ages, and was only regained in the sixteenth century, in England, due to Thomas Linacre (1460 ?- 1524) and John Caius (1510-1573).

The Renaissance in sixteenth century Europe, most active in Italy, revised anatomy and physiology, although the Church was reluctant to sanction departures from ancient texts, which, in medicine, were those of Aristotle and Galen.[13] Modern anatomy benefited from the practice of anatomical dissection, and permanent anatomy theatres were erected, the first being at Padua, in 1594, by Fabricius.[14] Animal experiments began the modern study of physiology.[15] The University of Padua was protected by nearby Venice, a wealthy and powerful city, usually independent of Rome. The tolerance of Padua in admitting Protestants attracted many foreign medical students, one of whom was Harvey (Fig. 7.1), who came in 1600, and obtained his medical degree in 1602. Fabricius, who taught Harvey, had published *De venarum ostiolis* in 1603.[16] The deduction by Harvey that these valves in the veins permitted blood flow only in one direction – towards the heart – led Harvey to his discovery of the circulation.[17]

Forerunners of Harvey

De Motu Cordis was the fruit of years of observations and experiments, many of which Harvey described in his annual Lumleian lectures (Fig. 7.2).[18] But ancient and more recent researchers had made significant contributions.[19]

Figure 7.1 The portrait of William Harvey in the Royal College of Physicians painted circa 1650. This Figure and Figs. 7.2-7.6 are reproduced from Chauncey D. Leake, 1941.

Erasistratus (330-245 B.C.) had traced the veins and arteries to the heart and described the auriculo-ventricular valves, but believed the arteries contained air.[20] Aristotle (384-322 B.C.) and Galen (131-200 A.D.) knew the arteries contained blood, but whilst Aristotle believed the heart was central to the supply of blood, Erasistratus and Galen thought that the liver continuously created blood.

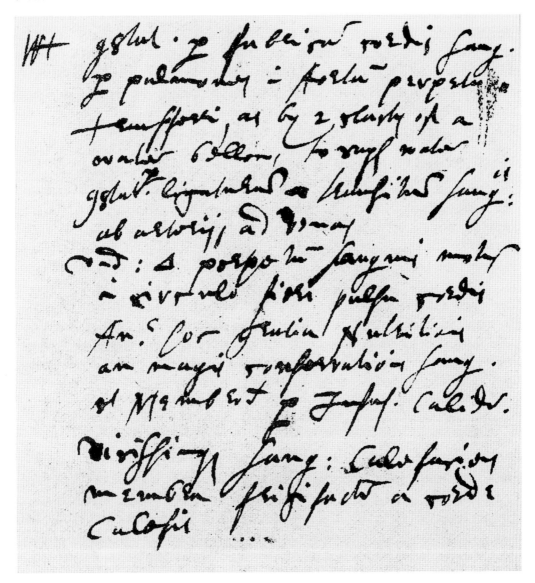

Figure 7.2 Harvey's first description of the circulation of the blood on p. 80 of his 1616 lecture notes. The Latin is in Harvey's hand and his initials appear top left.

The pulmonary circulation had been described in the thirteenth century by Ibn Nafis, a physician in Cairo, and a translation into Latin may have existed in the sixteenth century. This lesser circulation was also described by Servetus, who wrote : 'By a signal artifice ... the subtle blood is driven through the lungs and cleansed from its fumes, so at length it is stuff fit to become the vital spirit'.[21] For this and other heresies, Servetus was burnt alive in Geneva, in 1553, with nearly all of the thousand copies of his offending book, *Restitutio Christianismi*.[22] The modern anatomical concepts of Servetus have attracted much attention.[23] The pulmonary circulation was also known to Columbus (1516-1559) and Cesalpinus (1519-1603).[24] Servetus disproved Galen's statement that channels in the intraventricular septum permitted blood to pass between the ventricles, also doubted by Vesalius.[25] Nor could Leonardo da Vinci, who performed more than 100 autopsies, find Galen's pores.[26]

Supporters and Opponents of Harvey

De Motu Cordis was indifferently printed in Frankfurt with a small typeface on paper of poor quality (Fig. 3). There were numerous misprints due to difficult communications between author and printer: proofs were not sent and corrected.[27] But the science was revolutionary and, at first, attracted more criticism than praise. In England, James Primrose was Harvey's main opponent, but defence came from Robert Fludd, George Ent, Kenelm Digby, Thomas Bartholin, and Nathaniel Highmore.[28] Ole Worm in Copenhagen[29], Caspar Hofmann in Nuremberg[30], and Jean Riolan in Paris[31] were critics, but these were displaced by more worthy scientists, such as René Descartes, Johann Vesling, Frans de la Boe (Sylvius), and Jan de Wale. It is to this latter group, who examined the evidence at first hand, that Henry Power belongs. His support in 1652, based on a complete reappraisal of Harvey's observations and experiments, was important and welcome.

Sloane MS 1343, Circulatio Sanguinis, Inventio Harveiana

The manuscript consists of some 150 pages bound as a book (14 x 9 cms), written on both sides in English, in the hand of Power, whose signature often appears (Figs. 7.4 & 7.5).[32] The notes are divided into chapters and subdivided into 'experiments'. An experiment might be an operation on a living animal, usually a dog, but more often is an observation on a human or animal necropsy. Some 'experiments' are statements of received opinion. It is not always possible to determine whether Power is describing his own experiments and observations. Selections from the *MS* are described or quoted below :

Chapter 1. Explains how the laudable anatomical work of Aristotle and Galen has been extended, notably by 'our Reverend and Worthy Dr Harvey'

EXERCITATIO,
ANATOMICA DE
MOTV CORDIS ET SAN-
GVINIS IN ANIMALI-
BVS,
GVILIELMI HARVEI ANGLI,
Medici Regii, & Professoris Anatomiæ in Col-
legio Medicorum Londinensi.

FRANCOFVRTI,
Sumptibus GVILIELMI FITZERI.
ANNO M. DC. XXVIII.

Figure 7.3 Title page of the first 1628 edition of *De Motu Cordis*.

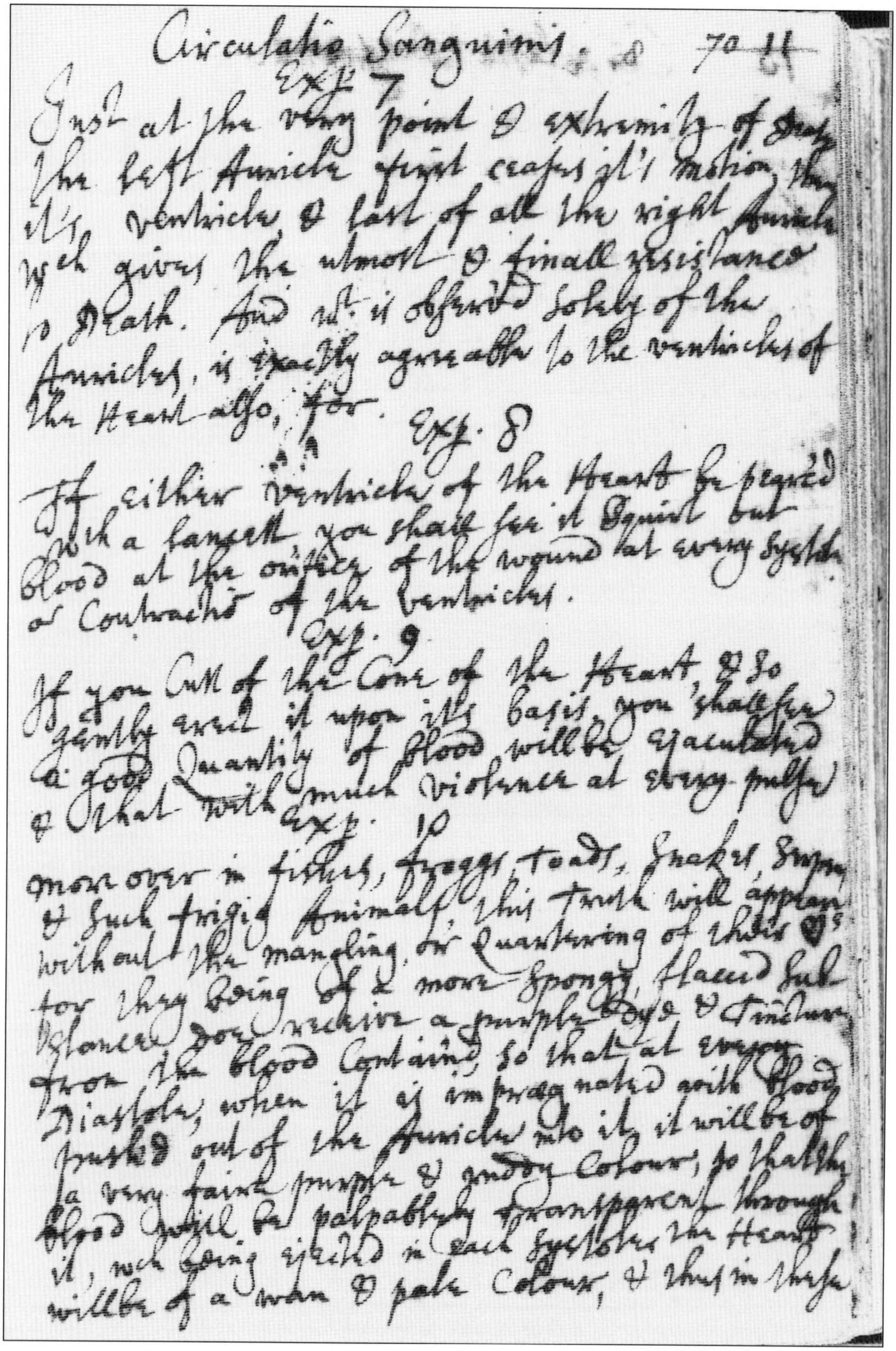

Circulatio Sanguinis. 8 70 11

Exp. 7

Just at the very point & extremity of death the left Auricle first ceases it's motion then it's ventricle, & last of all the right Auricle wch gives the utmost & finall resistance to Death. And wt is observed solely of the Auricles, is exactly agreeable to the ventricles of the Heart also, for.

Exp. 8

If either ventricle of the Heart be pierced with a lancett you shall see it squirt out blood at the orifice of the wound at every systole or Contraction of the ventricles.

Exp. 9

If you cutt of the Cone of the Heart, & so gently erect it upon its basis, you shall see a good Quantity of blood will be ejaculated & that with much violence at every pulse

Exp. 10

moreover in fishes, froggs, toads, snakes, serpents & such frigid Animals, this truth will appear without the mangling or Quartering of theis hearts for they being of a more spongy, flaccid substance doe receive a purple dye & tincture from the blood contained, so that at every Diastole, when it is impregnated with blood pushed out of the Auricle into it, it will be of a very faint purple & ruddy Colour, so that the blood will be palpably transparent through it, wch being ejected in each systole the Heart will be of a wan & pale Colour, & thus in these

Figure 7.4 Page 8 of Power's manuscript in the British Library, *Sloane MS 1343, f.8*. This page and that in Fig 7.5 are a selection of Power's experiments which replicated, most of Harvey's experiments and observations on the circulation of blood.

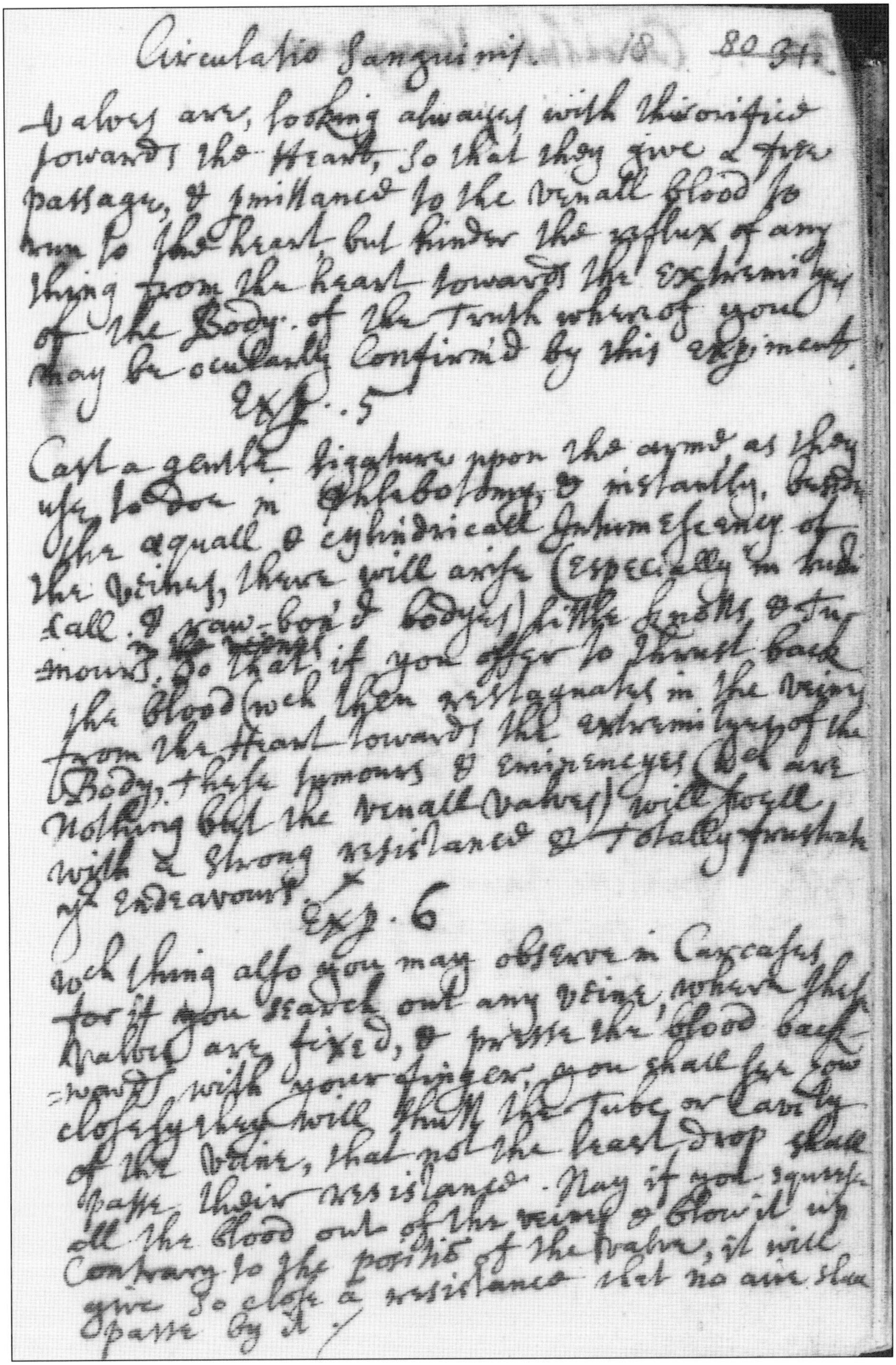

Circulatio Sanguinis. 18. 80 &c.

Valves are, looking alwayes with theirorifice towards the Heart, so that they give a free passage, & smittance to the venall blood to run to the heart, but hinder the reflux of any thing from the heart towards the extremityes of the Body. of the Truth whereof you may be ocularly confirm'd by this experiment.

Exp. 5

Cast a gentle ligature upon the armes as they use to doe in Phlebotomy & instantly, about the æquall & cylindricall Intumescency of the veines, there will arise (Especially in tall & raw-bon'd bodyes) little knotts, & tumours, so that if you offer to thrust back the blood (wch then restagnates in the veiny Body, & these tumours & eminenceyes wch are nothing but the venall valves) will swell with a strong resistance & totally frustrate yr endeavour.

Exp. 6

wch thing also you may observe in Carcases for if you search out any veine, where these valves are fixed, & presse the blood backwards with your finger, you shall see how closely they will shutt the Tube or Cavity of the veine, that not the least drop shall passe their resistance. Nay if you squeese all the blood out of the veine & blow it up contrary to the position of the valves, it will give so close a resistance that no aire shall passe by it.

Figure 7.5 Page 18 of Power's manuscript in the British Library, *Sloane MS 1343 F.18.*

who has 'the precedency for that Incomparable Invention of his, the Circulation of the Blood.' Anatomical studies are directed to areas hitherto obscure, but, above all, 'Living dissections ... by ocular Inspection to learn the abstrusity of hir [nature's] operations.'

Chapter 2. Describes opening the chest of a living animal and observing the 'Reciprocall motion and Quiescency which Anatomists call the contraction and Dilatation of the Heart.' In the slower heart beat of cold blooded animals such as amphibians, reptiles, and fishes the contraction and 'perisystole' [interval between systole and diastole] is more easily studied. In his interest in comparative anatomy, Power followed Harvey.[33] Power also describes the position and beat of the heart in the snail, louse, shrimp [probably Daphnia], crayfish, lobsters, crabs, and insects, but not in the bivalves (cockles, oysters and mussels), an error he shared with Harvey.[34]

> Experiment 8. 'If either ventricle of the Heart be pearc'd with a lancett, you shall see it squirt out blood ... at every systole or contraction of the ventricles'.

> Experiment 12. Dissect a living dogge ... cutt of the left ventricle, so that the septum cordis or Partition-wall of the Heart, may be clearly visible, then observe if the right ventricle ayt every pulse sqeeze any blood through the septum, to be received by the left ventricle, according to the conceits and conjectural whimseys of the Ancients, which you shall find to be absolutely false.[35]

> Experiment 14. Whilst the heart is in systole or contraction, all the arteries of the body pulse and are dilated.

> Experiment 16. The pulse of all the arteries of the body is simultaneous, and is caused by the movement of the blood from the heart at systole.

> Experiment 17. The pulse varies in frequency and vigour : 'Our experience comes closest to Cardan for wee have often tried by a minute-clock and found about 4000 pulses to passse in 1 hower'.

> Experiment 18. A cut into the pulmonary artery causes an escape of blood when 'the Right ventricle shrinks into contraction'.

> Experiment 19. 'Likewise if you Prick the Aorta, or any other artery ... you shall see the blood to jumpe out at every systole of the left ventricle ...'

> Experiment 21. From a transverse cut across the aorta of a dog, about half an ounce of blood is ejected at every pulse.

> Experiment 22. Exsanguination of a dog by cutting the carotid artery yields about 3 gallons of blood.[36]

> Experiment 27. If an artery is ligatured : 'you shall perceive a vehament

intumescency twixt the ligature and the heart, but on the other side of the ligature a manfest Detumescency ...'

Chapter 3. Of the veins and their valves.

Experiment 1. 'If you cast a ligature upon the vena cava, or any other veine ... the Intumescency and Detumescency will appeare just contrary to that in the Arteryes ...'

Experiment 2. Occlude a vein near a man's wrist by manual pressure. With another hand, massage the blood in the vein towards the heart. If you release the second pressure, the vein does not refill, whilst it does when the first pressure is removed. See Fig. 7.6 reproduced from Harvey's *De Motu Cordis*.

Experiment 3. In phlebotomy following a ligature on the arm, bleeding is profuse when the vein is opened <u>below</u> the ligature. If the vein is lanced <u>above</u> the ligature it does not bleed.

Experiments 4-7. Details the valves of the veins. 6. In 'Carcases' when you press the vein with a finger the blood will only travel towards the heart. If you inflate with air a vein emptied of blood the air also will only proceed towards the heart.

Experiments 8 & 9. Valves are not present in arteries, except at the beginnings of the pulmonary artery and the aorta.

Experiment 10. Power describes the ileocecal valve.

Experiment 11. Power describes a valve in the Eustachian tube, for which modern anatomists find no evidence.

Power then summarises his and Harvey's findings and description of the circulation. The contraction of left and right ventricles are simultaneous but the direction of the blood differs. From the right ventricle the blood passes to the lungs by the pulmonary artery, and by 'synastomoses or percribration through the spongy and porous substance of the lungs' enters the pulmonary veins and through the left auricle into the left ventricle. The contraction of the heart expels the blood into the aorta. The aortic valves prevent any retrograde flow and the blood 'is dispersed by the Branches, surcles and capillaryes of the Aorta, throughout every part of the body to be nourished.'
Power then turns to the:

> only mystery to compleate this Circulatory motion, yet to be discovered is to explaine by what means the arteriall blood insinuates itself into the veines and by what artifice and Contrivance in nature the Connection of these 2 Contrary motions is performed.

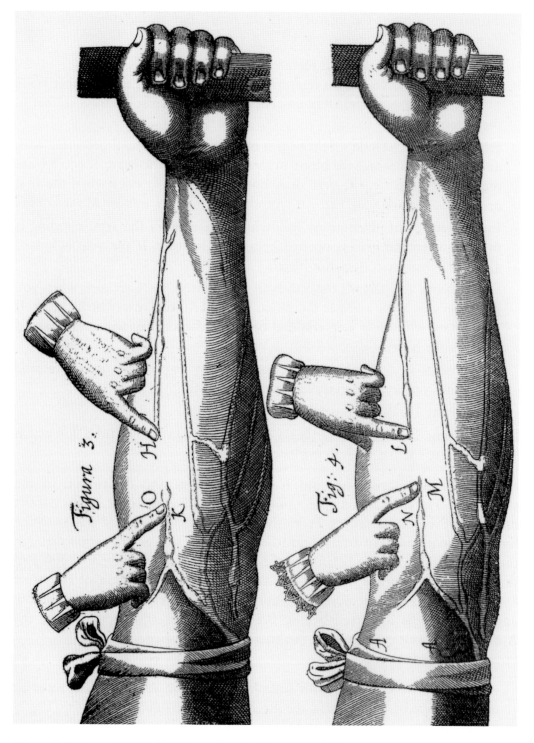

Figure 7.6 Figures 3 & 4 of *De Motu Cordis*, showing with figures 1 & 2 (not illustrated here) how the valves regulate the filling of the veins.

In this passage, Power repeats the difficulty raised by Harvey and which was only solved by the discovery of the capillaries by Malpighi in 1661. Power reviews Harvey's estimates of the volume of blood in a person and the rapidity of its circulation. The calculations are inaccurate by modern figures, but the importance is that only a circulation of the blood would agree with the observations.

Harvey and Power

The publication, in 1628, of *De Motu Cordis* by William Harvey is a turning point in medicine and biological sciences, when the outdated teaching of Aristotle and Galen began to be replaced by modern anatomy and physiology. The book, the fruit of many years of observations and experiments, established with certainty the circulation of the blood. The first reception was hostile, as the book overturned teaching held for hundreds of years, and backed by the authority of the Church. Henry Power, completing his medical studies in Cambridge, confirmed the observations and experiments of Harvey, in Cambridge, and at home in New Hall, Elland, near Halifax, Yorkshire. The British Library manuscript *Sloane MS 1343*, dated 1642, details the observations and experiments of Power confirming Harvey's discovery of the circulation of the blood. In England and in Europe many critics challenged the findings of Harvey. Of those who supported Harvey, importantly by repeating his work, a notable figure is Henry Power, whose work, described here, adds to his fame as a scientist and physician.

NOTES AND REFERENCES

1   The manuscript notebook of Henry Power, *Circulatio sanguinis Inventio Harveiana*, British Library, *Sloane MS 1343*.
2   Keynes, 6, p. 293.
3   Hughes, (2002).
4   For a description and illustrations of his house, New Hall, Elland, Halifax see Hughes (2003).
5   William Harvey. *Exercitatio Anatomica De Motu Cordis in Animalibus*, (Frankfurt, William Fitzeri, 1628), usually abbreviated to *De Motu Cordis*. Fitzer was an English publisher in Frankfurt, suggested to Harvey by Robert Fludd. See E. Weil, 'William Fitzer, the Publisher of Harvey's *De Motu Cordis*, 1628', *The Library*, (1943), 24, pp. 142-164.
6   In 1957, 300 years after Harvey's death, 'The William Harvey Issue' grouped articles in volume 12 of the *Journal of the History of Medicine and Allied Sciences* (henceforth *JHMAS*).
7   R. Willis, *The Works of William Harvey*, (London, Sydenham Society,

1847); C.D. Leake, *Anatomical Studies on the Motion of the Heart and the Blood*, a modern English translation of William Harvey's *De Motu Cordis*, (Springfield, Illinois, USA, Charles C. Thomas, 1928, 1931, & 1941); K.J. Franklin, *Movement of the Heart and Blood in Animals*, by William Harvey, translated from the Latin, (Oxford, Blackwell Scientific Publications, 1957); G. Whitteridge, *An Anatomical Disputation Concerning the Movement of the Heart and Blood in Living Creatures*, by William Harvey, translated from the Latin, (London, Blackwell Scientific Publications, 1976).

[8]   The many translations of Harvey's works are described by K.J. Franklin, 'On translating Harvey', *JHMAS*, pp. 114-119.

[9]   L. Chauvois, Two editions, translated into French, *Vie de William Harvey* (Paris, Editions Sedes, 1957), and into English, *The Life of William Harvey*, (London, Hutchinson, 1957); D'Arcy Power, *William Harvey*, (London, T. Fisher Unwin, 1897); G. Keynes, *The Life of William Harvey*, (Oxford, The Clarendon Press, 1978).

[10] Galen described the cardiovascular system in *On Anatomical Procedures*, Book VII, translated by C. Singer, (London, Wellcome Foundation, 1956), pp. 172-200, and in *De Usu Partium*, Books VI & VII.

[11] The latin *arteria* means windpipe.

[12] Wilfrid Bonser, 'General Medical practice in Anglo-Saxon England', In *Science, Medicine, and History*, two volumes, edited by E.A. Underwood, (London, Oxford University Press, 1953), 1, pp. 154-163.

[13] C.D. O'Malley, 'Medical Education during the Renaissance', in *The History of Medical Education*, edited by C.D. O'Malley, (Berkeley, Los Angeles, London, 1970), pp. 89-102.

[14] Girolamo Fabrizi d'Acquapendente, Professor of Anatomy during Harvey's medical studies at Padua.

[15] For an analysis of Harvey's experiments see J.J.R. Macleod, 'Harvey's experiments on circulation', *Annals of Medical History*, (1928), 10, pp. 338-348.

[16] Fabricius, *De venarum ostiolis*, (1603), edited by K.J. Franklin, Springfield, Illinois, 1933. Earlier anatomists had described the valves. See J.O. Leibowitz, 'Early accounts of the valves in the veins', *JHMAS*, pp. 189-196.

[17] Conversation of Harvey with Boyle. See H. Cohen, 'The Germ of an idea or what put Harvey on the scent', *JHMAS*, pp. 102-105; and J.J. Byleby, 'Boyle and Harvey on the Valves in the Veins', *Bulletin of the History of Medicine*, (1982), 56, pp. 351-367.

[18] For a detailed account of Harvey's work see H.P. Bayon, *Annals of Science*, (1938), Parts I & II, 3, pp. 59-118; (1938), Part III, 3, pp. 435-456; and (1939), Part IV, 4, pp. 65-106.

19 H. Rolleston, 'Harvey's Predecessors and Contemporaries', *Annals of Medical History*, (1928), 10, pp. 323-337.

20 Erasistratus of Ceos founded the school of anatomy in Alexandria. Aristotle of Stagiri, was a pupil in Plato's academy in Athens, where he became a teacher. Galen of Pergamon studied in Smyrna, Corinth and Alexandria, and moved to Rome, where he practised as a physician.

21 D. Guthrie, 'The Evolution of Cardiology', in *Science, Medicine, And History*, 2 volumes, edited by E.A. Underwood, (London, Oxford University Press, 1953, 2, pp. 508-517.

22 Three copies of *Restitutio Christianismi* survive, in Vienna, Paris, and Edinburgh.

23 William Osler, 'Michael Servetus', *Johns Hopkins Hospital Bulletin*, (1910), 21, pp. 1-11; C.D. O'Malley, Michael Servetus (1511?-1553), *A translation of his Geographical, Medical, and Astrological Writing*, (Berkeley, Los Angeles, USA, University of California Press, 1953).

24 Mattheus Realdus Columbus of Cremona was the pupil of Vesalius at Padua. Andreas Cesalpino of Arezzo taught at Pisa and Rome.

25 Vesalius' reservations on septal pores were published in the second edition of *De Fabrica Humani Corporis*, (1555), Book VI. See C.D. O'Malley, *Andreas Vesalius of Brussels*, (Berkley, Los Angeles, and London, University of California Press, 1965), pp. 280-281.

26 C.D. O'Malley and J.B. de C.M. Saunders, *Leonardo da Vinci on the human body*, (New York, Henry Schuman, 1952), pp. 216-217.

27 Communication between author and publisher was hampered by the Thirty Years War (1618-1648).

28 For the literature from 1628-1657 see E. Weil, 'The Echo of Harvey's *De Motu Cordis* (1628)' *JHMAS*, pp. 167-174. Power appears in 1652.

29 E. Gotfredsen, 'The Reception of Harvey's Doctrine in Denmark', *JHMAS*, pp. 202-208.

30 E.V. Ferrario, 'William Harvey's Debate with Caspar Hofmann on the Circulation of the Blood', *JHMAS*, (196O), 15, pp. 7-21.

31 Lazare Rivière (Riverius) at Montpellier opposed Riolan and defended Harvey. Weil, p. 172.

32 A transcript of the manuscript appears in F.J. Cole, 'Henry Power on the Circulation of the Blood', *JHMAS*, pp. 291-324.

33 F.J. Cole, 'Harvey's Animals', *JHMAS*, pp. 106-113.

34 All these bivalves have a well developed contracting heart.

35 The absence of communication between the ventricles through the septum was essential in refuting Galen's account of the circulation.

36 For a dog this seems excessive, but the point is: blood must circulate, otherwise a large quantity would have to be created and consumed.

Chapter 8

Power's use of the Telescope and Microscope

Should you stranger be disposed to discredit this panegeric, know that Power's pre-eminence in learning had long been evidenced as well in other branches of Philosophy and Medicine, as in investigations with the microscope, and the discovery of the properties of quicksilver. His name indeed will for ever be a household word, and will deservedly command the respect of learned men. Not merely in the destruction of the germs of diseases has his reputation been achieved, but from the evidences of his learning which have been brought to light. His years were few, his learning great.[1]

Chapter 6 began with a translation of the first part of the Latin on the brass plate in All Saints, Wakefield, where Power was buried on December the 23rd, 1668. Above is the translated second half of the inscription. The writer was familiar with Power's breadth of scientific enquiry : a substantial addition to his competence as a physician. Power possessed both telescopes and microscopes and his observations through these instruments were among the first in England. He was the first practical microscopist in England, where his *Experimental Philosophy* was the first publication on the subject.

History of the Telescope and Microscope

The development of the telescope and the compound microscope proceeded in parallel, as their optics are similar, both requiring two or more lenses.[2] The simple microscope, consisting only of a single lens, has a much longer history. Seneca (*circa* AD 63) wrote : 'Letters, however small and dim ... are comparatively large and distinct when seen through a glass globe filled with water'.[3] The mathematics of the optical properties of curved glasses were known to Euclid (3rd century BC) and Ptolemy (2nd century AD) and this knowledge was preserved and added to by the Arab Alhazen (d. 1038 AD).[4] In the 16th century concave as well as convex glasses began to be made by scientists such as Leonardo da Vinci (1452-1519) and Francesco Maurolico (1494-1575). Advances in resolution came with lenses of short focal length, which required the expert grinding and polishing of lenses, in which Anthony van Leeuwenhoeck excelled. His tiny lenses, of very short focal length and expertly mounted, began to approach the maximal resolution of a simple microscope. Leeuwenhoeck's observations of the minute natural world are justifiably famous.

Meanwhile the compound microscope was being developed in parallel with the telescope. Spectacles were now being made in the Netherlands and, in a shop in Middleburg, which made and sold these spectacles, a boy named Zacharias, *circa* 1580, discovered the principle of the telescope by mounting two lenses in a tube.[5] Zacharias and his father, Hans, also made the first compound microscopes.[6] [7] This discovery of a convex and a concave lens arranged in a tube was taken up by Galileo Galilei, who was the first to describe the path taken by rays of light through two lenses, and is rightly considered to be the inventor of the telescope.[8] In 1611, Johannes Kepler followed Gallileo with a clearer account of the optics of a telescope.[9] The first practical use of a compound microscope was made by the astronomer Francisco Fontana of Naples who, in 1646, published his *New Observations of the Things in Heaven and Earth*.[10] The eighth tractate describes his use of a compound microscope, which he claims to have invented in 1628. The work of Christopher Scheiner, René Descartes, Athanasius Kircher, Philippo Buonanni, and Malpighi requires mention before we arrive at the microscope in England. [11] [12] [13] [14] [15]

Towards the middle of the seventeenth century, many instrument makers flourished in London, and several turned their talents to the design and construction of telescopes and microscopes. These makers of optical instruments originated as technical assistants to scientists but began to be independent optical specialists offering a commercial service. Essential was the accurate grinding of lenses from high quality lead glass, hitherto a speciality of Venice. Giuseppe Campani of Rome was famous for his fine telescopes and microscopes but now the London makers were producing excellent instruments. Power dealt with Richard Reeve, the best known of many. Reeve came from a landed Berkshire family and his early trade was turning ivory into decorative pieces.[16] [17] [18] About 1640, he began to make lenses for the mathematician John Pell and this led to making and supplying optical instruments to scientists from his shop 'over against the Foot and Leg in Long Acre', London. The main custom was telescopes to the astronomers in Gresham College and the Royal Society in London, and to astronomers in Oxford, where Seth Ward had created an observatory in Wadham College. Power purchased a telescope (or telescopes) from Reeves, as is evident from a letter from Reeves dated 11th March :

I have received yr letter … in wch you resolved to adventure on ye glass of 12 foote erected & inverted with convexes wch according to yr command I have sent with directions how to use it pasted to ye several parts of ye tube ye round piece yt ye inverting glasses are in is written within ye drawer as well as on ye outside. Ye purpose of them is to observe ye planets. If you would see them without rays you must use an aperture yt does not lett in too much light. But when you will see the

Pliades or ye milky way then ye biggest aperture is to be used. When you observe ye Sunn you must look through a dark and coloured glass, of wch sort I have enclosed & sent you two wch may be held next ye eye to keepe ye sun's Beams from offending it.

Astronomical Observations

Sun spots, Comet, Comments on Astrology

Power not only purchased microscopes but also assisted in their design.[19] He wrote on the 10th of August 1662 (Fig. 8.1), complimenting Reeves on his microscopes but adding :

> ... though in all of them there are some deficiencies which I heartily wish your further skill & experience could rectifye, as first :
> 1. That the Microscope takes in so very little of the object if distinctly seen that nothing but minute things can well be discerned therein.
> 2. the object glass stands so very neare the object plate that many things cannot be layd theron for observation unless the brass screw be of very great height.
> 3. why may it not advantage the fabric of the Microscope if the eyeglass and middle glass were made to change their distances, as well as the middle and object glass does.
> 4. I would have a Chrystall object plate that some Bodyes might be seene through, which the opacity of the object plate now hinders.
> 5. I would have severall sorts of object glasses because I thinke some may more distinctly represent some sort of objects than others.
> 6. why may not 2 convexes serve the Microscope & be as powerful to represent as 3.

> If you have or can any way advantage the fabric of the Microscope by these small hints I pray you let me know & what might be the price of an exceedingly good one.

In 1661, Power was writing to his old acquaintance Dr Robinson that there were four microscopes in Halifax '... as good as the world affordes'. Possibly in some museum, one of Power's microscopes survives, but at least we have his description of his microscope and instructions for its use. This is contained in a manuscript, dated 1661, that was included in the manuscripts which became the book *Experimental Philosophy*, but this passage was not included in the book.[20] As it is the first extensive English description of a microscope it is reproduced in full below :

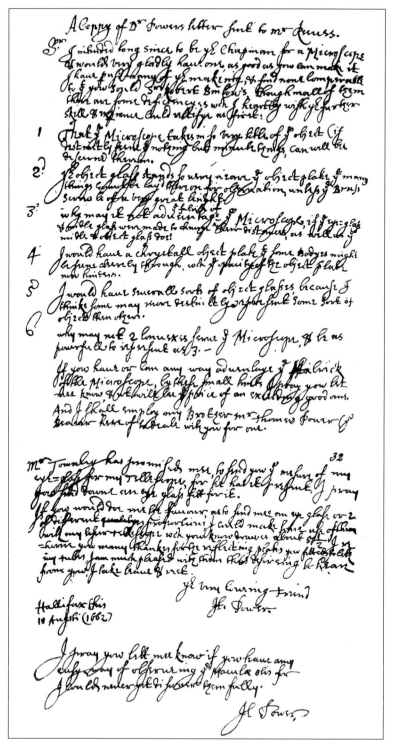

Figure 8.1 Copy of a letter from Power to Reeves dated 10th August, 1662.
In *Sloane 1396 f31-32* and reproduced in Clay, RS. and Court, TH., 1934.

Power's Description of His Microscope

This microscope consists of three glasses

1. The object glass
2. The middle glass
3. The eye glass

1. The object glass is a little glass & is in that small brass houell which you may take of and on at the end of the long brass screw.
2. The middle glass is that faire round convex glass which is placed in the middle of the tube with the brass ring about the edge of it which is to keep it fast in its place for shogging or falling out.
3. The eye glass is that which is placed towards the top of the tube & is a little double convex glass (about the bigness of a shilling). It is called the eye glass because it is nearest the eye when you looke through the microscope at any object.

About these glasses you must observe that you keep them from any oyl or grease touching them (which will stain & spot their clearness & diaphanity) you must wipe them with a clean handkerchief from any dust or misty vapour that soyle them , & remember to keep the microscope in a dry place, else the dampy mosysture will spoyl them. It is not much matter wheather side of the glass be layd upwards, when you have dried them and put them nigh the tube againe.

The tube in which all these glasses are placed consists of 3 parts. The top screw or Head-screw of 2 parts. The body of 2 parts (an inward & outward cylinder). The foot-screw or Pedistall.

1. The top screw is the short screw to which the eye is placed which being taken of, the eyeglass appears. The second pair of it being taken of the middle glass appears, which is fastened to a cylinder that moves up and down in the body which by drawing up & down (when you look through the Microscope) will greaten or lessen the object as you please.
2. The body is the outermost leather cylinder to the bottom of which is fastened the brass screw with the houell screw, the object glass is put on the end of it.
3. Lastly the pedistall or foot screw is the part which hath 3 brass Leggs & screws of or on from the brass screw or higher or lower as you please. In the bottom of this pedistall is a round hole which is covered with the object plate which is that black piece of wood that moves every way & the middle of which is let in that small round piece of ivory so that you may set the object either upon the white ivory or the black Cedar as shall be seen better for some objects appeare better upon a dark ground & and some upon a white.

If the brass screw be too glad you may rubb it with a bit of beeswax & that will harden it at any time. Thus much for the description of the microscope.

The use of the Microscope

1st. Having wiped the glass clean & set them in their due places & Having screwed all the parts of the Microscope together lay the object on the object-plate (suppose a little sand) then laying the eye close to the top of the tube looke through the tube moving the screw higher or lower till you find the object at the best distance to be seene, then you may draw up the inward cylinder out of the Body higher or lower as you please which will greaten or lessen the object as you please.

Note 1st. That you will see nothing considerably well but in a clear light. I sometimes use with a burning glass to strike a full light upon the object plate where the object lies & so can see it most lively.

2nd. That you can but see little small animals the best & clearest because this glass will but take in a very little object at once. I neede say no more, only I have sent this little Box of such things I looke often at, & I know will ... * Can rectify your mistakes in any thing. Your servant H.Power

* Words cannot be discerned.

NOTES AND REFERENCES

1   Translated from the Latin inscription in Wakefield Cathedral.
2   Singer, C. 'Notes on the Early History of Microscopy', *Proceedings of the Royal Society*, Section of the History of Medicine, 7, 1914, pp. 247-279.
3   Lucius Annaeus Seneca. *Quaestiones Naturales*, book 1, chapter vi.
4   Alhazen. *Thesaurus Opticae*. A Latin translation by Gerard of Cremona in 1542.
5   Zacharias was the son of a spectacle maker in the Netherlands. See A.J. van der Aas, Biograpisch Woodenboek de Nederlande Negende, Harlem, 1880.
6   Evidence of these microscopes is that examples were presented to Prince Maurice, governor of the United Dutch forces and to the Austrian Archduke Albert, supreme governor of Holland. See Pierre Borel, *De vero telescopi inventore cum brevi omnium conspicillorum historia*, The Hague, 1655, p. 34 ff.
7   These early microscopes are described and illustrated in Schott, C. *Magia universalis*, 1656.
8   Gallilei, G. *Il Saggiatore nel quale conbilancia esquisita e giusta si ponderano le cose contenute nella Libra astronomica e filosofica di Lotaris Sarsi Sigensans*, Rome, 1623, p. 62.

[9] Kepler, J. *Dioptrice, seu Demonstratio eorum quae visui et visibilibus propter conspicilla non ita pridem inventa accidunt*, Cologne, 1511, See problemata 86 and 87.

[10] Fontana, F. *Novae Caelestium terrestriumque rerum obsevationes et fortasse hactenus non vulgatae a Francisto Fontana specillis a se inventis er ad summam perfectionem productis editae*, Naples, 1646.

[11] Scheiner, C. *Rosa Ursina sive sol ex admirando facularum et macularum suarum Phaenomeno varius.*, 1626-1630. Quoted in Singer, p. 163-164.

[12] Descartes, R. *La Dioptrique*, 9th discourse. Published as an appendix to the *Discours de la Méthode,* Leyden, 1637.

[13] Kircher, A. *Ars Magna Lucis et Umbrae*, Rome, 1646, p. 835.

[14] Buonanni, P. *Museum Kircherianum*, Rome, 1709.

[15] Malpighi, M. *De Externo Tactus Organo Anatomica Observatio*. Naples, Aegidium Longum, 1685.

[16] Taylor, E.G.R. *The Mathematical Practitioners of Tudor and Stuart England*, Cambridge, Institute of Navigation, Cambridge University Press, 1954.

[17] Simpson, A.D.C. 'Richard Reeve – the "English Campani" – and the Origins of the London Telescope-making Tradition', *Vistas in Astronomy*, 28, pp. 357-365, 1985.

[18] Simpson, A.D.C. 'Robert Hooke and Practical Optics : Technical Support at a Scientific Frontier'. In, *Robert Hooke : New Studies*, edited by M. Hunter and S. Schaffer, ?London, The Boydell Press, 1989.

[19] Letters between Power and Reeve are in *Sloane, 1396, f. 31-32*. They are reproduced in Clay, R.S. and Court, T.H. 'Note of the introduction of the Field Lens in the Microscope ; Dr Henry Power and his Letters', *Journal of the Royal Microscopical Society*, 54, 1934, pp. 23-28.

[20] British Library, *Sloane 1393*.

Chapter 9

Observations in Natural History

To the generous Virtuosi, and Lovers of Experimental Philosophy.
Certainly this World was made not onely to be inhabited, but studied and
contemplated by Man ; and, How few are there in the World that perform
this homage due to their creator ?

In this quotation from his book, Power sets out with some force man's
obligation to study the world about him.[1] He is chiefly addressing the 'Virtuosi'
and despairs of the incurious many, whose understanding is comparable to that
of 'Pugs and Baboons' :

There is a world of People indeed, and but few Men in it ; mankind is but
preserv'd in a few Individuals ; the greatest part of Humanity is lost in
Earth, and their Souls so fixed in that grosser moity of themselves (their
bodies) that nothing can volatilize them and set their Reasons at Liberty.
The numerous Rabble that seem to have the Signatures of Man in their
faces, are Brutes in their understanding, and have nothing of the nobler
part that should denominate their Essences ; tis by the favour of a
Metaphor we call them Men, for at best they are but ... the moving
frames, and Zanies of men, and have nothing but their outsides to justifie
their titles to Rationality.

Power's strictures were directed also to the students and professors of the
universities. A student could graduate :

... if he could but stiffly wrangle out a vexatious dispute of some
Peripatetick qualities, or the like ; which (if translated into English)
signified no more that a Heat 'twixt two Oyster-wives in Billingsgate.

Nor were the 'Purple Gowns of Learning' free from fault. When the professors
have arrived at a competent height in any Art or Science : 'if any difficulty do
arise ... they instantly pronounce it as a thing impossible to be done...'
Chemistry is rubbished by the philosopher's stone, and Mechanics by the
perpetual motion machine. Astronomers are baffled by the motion of the
comets and Geographers are reminded of their areas of Terra Incognita.
Physicians (like himself) have critics, who deny the circulation of the blood, but
also remark on 'the incurability of Cancers and Quartans'. In addition to the
bickering between educated men '... there is one more general impediment,

which is an Authentic discouragement to the promotion of the Arts and Sciences …'. because of the prevalent belief in the decay of the World.

Power, when he wrote these words, was consolidating his career in experimental science and observations of natural history. But soon his medical practice, the supervision of the alterations to his house in Elland, and the care of his family were diverting him from medical and scientific research. Also in Halifax and later in Wakefield, apart from Richard Towneley in Burnley, he had no colleagues who shared his interests. But what he had achieved is notable. His experiments have been reviewed in chapters 5-8. Here we describe his observations in natural history. Examples of these are reproduced in Figures 9.1-9.6. Most physicians were acquainted with medicinal herbs but Power had a deeper knowledge of botany, to the study of which he brought his microscope. The study of the taxonomy of plants was now well advanced, and both native species and those imported from Europe and the New World were studied in botanic gardens. What was poorly understood was the life history of plants. The metabolism of plants was debated, as was whether they exhibited sexual dimorphism. The reproductive structures of flowers were being described without much understanding of their function. Ferns, not possessing flowers, were of interest, as seemingly they did not bear any of the seeds and fruits, which in other plants were of the greatest importance.

Power studied a variety of seeds and fruits.[2] Some were present in 'large Pulps' as in the seed of 'all pomiferous plants'. Others, 'besides the circum-involving Pulpe, are immured in Shells as all Stone-Fruit'. Mulberries and Raspberries had seeds within the 'Pulp' but in strawberries 'Nature hath put out the Seeds, as if they were sprouting from the Pulp'. The seeds of the corn poppy were reniform, with a surface like a honeycomb '… with regular Sides and Angles, making all of them pentagonal and hexagonal …'. In a yellow lily Power saw the pistil – 'a long style or poyntel' surrounded with stamens '… small chives which are tipped with pendents…'. On every 'pendent' was '… a small Dust or Powder, which will cleave to and smut your fingers…'. Under the microscope this was of a golden colour, whilst that from a white lily was '… of a pure pale yellow, and like so many pieces of polished Amber'. Power examined the leaves of several species of plants. The underside of the leaf of the sweet brier was '… diaper'd most excellently with silver', whilst the under surface of a nettle was '… all full of Needles …' Every needle had '… a Crystal pummel, so that it looks like a sword …'. The whole leaf under the microscope looked like '… a Sword-Cutler's Shop, full of glittering drawn Swords, Tucks and Daggers …'.

Power examined many invertebrate species with his microscope.[3] The structure of the flea was an early study. Enlarged, it appeared as 'a little prawn

---

OBSERVAT. XI.

Another Field-Spider.

I Took a Field-Spider under a ſtone, 13. of *June*, with a bag of eggs faſtned to her tayl, bigger than all the bulk of her body ; I opened it, and ſaw abundance of blewiſh eggs in it, which in the *Microſcope* look'd white and round, like your counterfeit pearl, and I could moſt clearly ſee abundance of very minute Spiders, newly hatch'd, no bigger, and juſt like Mites in Meal, with white hairs and briſtles, eſpecially in their tail, creeping and crawling amongſt the eggs : The Nett-work of the Purſe or Bag ſeem'd all diaphanous ; a very pleaſant ſpectacle, and of curious workmanſhip.

I then made the like Obſervation of a bag full of Houſe-Spider-eggs, which are round and white, juſt like white Poppy feed; and all things look'd whitiſh, and ſomething Tranſparent therein alſo : but the youngling Spiders (that were either hatching, or newly hatch'd) were far bigger then the former, and white as Alablaſter, but ſhap'd like the Parent with five legs on each ſide (without hairs or briſtles) and not by far ſo active as the other. I could not ſee any Heart beat in any of them all.

Figure 9.1 This Figure and Figs. 9.2-9.7 are from *Experimental Philosophy*. This is from page 15.

or shrimp'. Through the cornea of the two prominent eyes the pupil appeared as ' a round blackish spot' surrounded by a 'greenish glistering circle, which is the Iris, (as vibrant and glorious as a Cats eye) ...'. Power describes the very long neck 'which he could nimbly move anyway'. The head, body and limbs are clad in polished, black armour added to by hairs and bristles. The feet have 'claws or talons'. The prominent proboscis penetrates the skin to suck blood. The flea has great strength displayed by drawing a large brass pin inserted into the tail. Next is a description of a honey bee and the 'great Humble-Bee'. The eye is

OBSERVAT. XVI.

The red Mite, found on Spiders.

THere is a red Mite which you shall often find feeding upon Spiders ; She is bodied just like a Tortoise, with a little head and six long small leggs, three on each side: About the leggs of the Field-Spider I have found many of these Coral-Mites or Tortoises, and this thing I have observed of them, That they cling exceeding close to the Animal whilst she is alive ; but when dead, they all fall off and creep away from her, as lice do from dying men, or other vermin from an old rotten falling house.

Figure 9.2 From *EP*, p.19.

studied both *in situ*, and after removal by dissection. Removing the head of the bee allowed a view of the beating heart : ' ... a white pulsing vesicle.' The sting was examined : '... hollow and tubulous like a Shoomaker's punch so that when they prick the flesh , they do also, through that channel, transfuse the poison into it ...'. The structure of the house fly is described in great detail, with especial attention to the eye, an element which Power especially examines. He examines the eye of many species of 'fly' such as the butterfly, mayfly, dragonfly, horsefly, and those that 'feed' on cow-dung. The parts of the butterfly have especial study with speculation as to their function. Moving on from observing flies, Power examines the louse and compares his observations with those of Thomas Moufflet and William Harvey.[4] As did these earlier observers, Power saw the beating of the heart : '... this motion of *Systole* and *Diastole* is most palpably seen... ' and piercing the heart – 'I prick'd the white vesicle with a small needle and let out a little drop of blood' – caused the death of the louse.

Power examined several species of spider and correctly described that they have eight legs, a head joined to the thorax [a cephalothorax] and four, six or eight eyes.[5] He described two species of house spider. His 'little white Field-Spider with short legs' with eight eyes is clearly a crab spider, and possibly either *Mitsumena vatia* or the more common *Xysticus cristatus*. There are

OBSERVAT. XVII.

The Mites or Lice found on Humble-Bees.

Within that yellow plufh or furre of Humble-Bees you fhall often find a little whitifh very nimbly-running Animal, which hath the fhape and form of a Mite in the *Microfcope* : I remember the Induftrious *Kircher* fayes, he hath found by his Glaffes Lice upon Fleas : Either our Fleas in *England* are not like theirs in *Italy* for this property, or elfe I have never taken them in their Lowfie feafon : But I fee no reafon to the contrary, but both Fleas and Lice may have other Lice that feed upon them, as they do upon us. For fince the minuteft Animal that comes within the reach of our *Microfcope*, is found to have a mouth, ftomack, and gutts, for Nutrition ; and moft, if not all, the *Parenchymata* for Circulation and Separation of Excrements, there can be no doubt, but they have alfo a continual perfpiration and exudation through the habit of their body : Of which excrement of the third and laft Concoction, all thefe Vermin that pefter the outfide of Animals, are generated.

Figure 9.3 From *EP*, p.20.

several possibilities for his 'Field Spider with long Legs' but the description would fit *Tibellus oblongus*. His 'Field-Spider under a stone' would be a wolf spider, which spins no web. Examined on the 13th of June this female had 'a bag of eggs fastened to her tayl...'. Spiders can harbour mites and Power described a red mite with six legs. Mites were also seen on Bumble bees. In ponds, Power observed the larval form of mosquitoes (or other insects) as 'little whitish Animals, which move up and down the water with jerks'. Cheese, meal, wax, and rotten wood harboured maggots of several varieties. One larval form, probably then common, was the glow-worm described as 'that Night-Animal with its Lanthorn in its tail; that creeping-Star, which seems to outshine those of the Firmament ...' Grasshoppers were now described with close attention to their eyes, as were ants, whose provident ways were commented upon. The description of 'Cuckow-Spitt' has literary merit :

> That spumeous froth or dew ... which is most frequently found in Lavander-Beds, Hors-mint, *etc*, looks like a heap of glass-bubbles ... in which you shall always find a little Grub, or Animal, which in the *Microscope* seems a pretty golden-coloured Insect, with three leggs on each side ; and two horns, and two round fair goggle-eyes of a duskish red colour, like polished Rubies; which you may also see latticed and perforated in a clear light.[6]

Power's 'Cow-Lady, or spotted Scarabee' and 'a very lively and nimble Animal' is the ladybird. Having removed and mounted the head in wax, the 'two little small black eyes' were each 'set between three white plates, like polished Ivory' and '... curiously lattic'd like those in a Fly formerly described.' Removing the 'spotted short crustaceous wings' (the wing coverts) revealed the 'pair of filmy Tiffany long wings, like those of Flyes'. Removing the wings exposed the 'thin tender black skin' through which the pulsation of the heart could be seen, beating for 12 or 14 hours after decapitation. 'The Water-Insect, or Water-Spider, which moves nimbly upon the water' is probably the water boatman. The Royal Society was intrigued by Power's studies of 'little white Eels or Snigs, in Vineger or Aleger', found when these liquids have 'arrived to some peculiar temper or putrefaction'.[7] They can be observed in two or three drops of liquid on a glass laid on the object plate of the microscope, but also with the 'bare eye' in a tube of 'Venice-glass'. They resemble 'so many shreds of the purest Dutch thread' making 'a great shoal or mass of quick Eels or Hair-worms'. They die when the liquid dries or is heated but survive freezing after which 'all my animals ... danced and frisked about as lively as ever'.

The four eyes of a 'great Black Snail' (probably a slug) were examined and dissection exposed 'a whole Sett of the same parts and organs with other Animals, as Heart, Liver, Spleen, Stomach, Guts, Mouth and Teeth, Veins and Arteries...'.[8] Power observed that this 'creature hath also a circulation of its nutritive humour, which is to it as Bloud is to other Animals.'

Concluding this cornucopia of observations is a detailed description of the lamprey,[9] again with attention to the heart, the auricle, and the circulation :

> In this Animal, you may easily distinguish between the motion of the heart and auricle, for there intercedes the time of a pulse twixt the motion of the auricle and the heart; and the heart in every diastole is of a fair purple and ruddy colour, and in every systole pale and wan, as is observable in Frogs and other Fishes also; where you may see the heart to

OBSERVAT. XXV.

Of Cuckow-Spitt, and the little Infect bred therein, in May.

THat spumeous froth or dew(which here in the North we call Cuckow-Spittle, and, in the South, Wood-fear; and which is most frequently found in Lavander-Beds, Horf-mint,&c.)looks like a heap of glafs-bubbles, or a knob'd drinking-glafs; in which you fhall always find a little Grub, or Animal, which in the *Microfcope* feems a pretty golden-coloured Infect, with three leggs on each fide; and two horns,and two round fair goggle-eyes of a duskifh red colour,like polifh'd Rubies; which you may alfo fee latticed and perforated in a clear light. Her tayl is all jemmar'd with Annulary divifions, which at laft end in a ftump, which fhe often draws up, or thrufts out, at her pleafure.

Muffet, de Infect. Cap. 16. pag.122. *Muffet* cals this Infect, *Locuftellam*, or, a puny-Locuft; and faith, That firft it creepeth, then leapeth, and at laft flyeth. She has two blackifh claws, or pounces (at the ends of her feet,) which fhe can open and fhut at her pleafure: We could difcover no mouth at all, but a long reddifh Probe, between the fore-legs, through which, perchance, fhe fuck'd her froathy nourifhment.

Now, what this fpumeous matter is, and into what Animal this Infect is at laft fhaped or tranfpeciated, are Doubts that as yet have found no clear and experimental Decifion.

That the Spattle is a froathy kind of dew that falls

from

Figure 9.4 From *EP*, p.28.

OBSERVAT. XLI.

Corn Poppy Seeds.

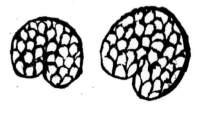

THey are none of them globular, nor of a smooth surface, but all like Kidneys in form, and of the seeming bignefs of Walnuts, and like an Hony-Comb on the furface, with regular Sides and Angles, making all of them pentagonal and hexagonal areola's ; and gliftering in the Sun-fhine like Tiffue, or the Foil on the backfide of a Looking-glafs, as is prefented in thefe two Figures. Some other Seeds alfo looked not unlike them, as Henbane, Flower of Briftow, &c.

Figure 9.5 From *EP*, p.49.

OBSERVAT. XLV.

Of Nettles.

LOok at the backfide of a Nettle-Leaf, and you fhall fee it all full of Needles, or rather long fharp tranfparent Pikes, and every Needle hath a Cryftal pummel, fo that it looks like a Sword-Cutler's Shop, full of glittering drawn Swords, Tucks, and Daggers ; fo that here you may autoptically fee the Caufes, as well as you have formerly felt the Effects, of their Netling. Something like them, appear the Prickles on Borrage-Leafs and Stalks.

Figure 9.6 From *EP*, p.51.

OBSERVAT. XLVII.

A Nitt.

A Nitt is an Egge glewed by some viscous matter to the sides of the hair it sticks to ; it is Oval in shape, white in colour , and full of transparent Liquor or Gelly , and seems to be cased in a brittle Shell by the crackling it makes 'twixt your nails. In the same manner appears a Nitt in a Horse's hair : *Muffet* will needs have it a quick , or rudely-shaped Animal. Thus discursive Argumentation and Rational probabilities mislead men in the Wilderness of Enquiry ; but he that travels by the Clew , which his own sense and ocular observation has spun out , is likeliest to trace the secureft path , and go furthest into the Maze and Labyrinth of Truth.

Figure 9.7 From *EP*, p.52.

shift colours by turns, as it receives or ejects the bloud in the performance of the circulation.

The above quotations indicate how profound were Power's observations on the natural world. The eyes of invertebrates attracted his particular attention as did their hearts and circulation. Following Harvey, he was confirming that the circulation of the blood occurred throughout the animal kingdom.

NOTES AND REFERENCES

[1] *Experimental Philosophy, pp. 183-193.*

[2] Ibid, pp. 46-51

[3] Ibid, pp. 1-36.

[4] Mouffet, T. *Insectorum sive Minimorum Animalum Theatrum*. This MS., dated *c*. 1590, is in the British Library, *Sloane MS. 4014*. It was published by Sir Theodore de Mayerne in 1634.

[5] *Experimental Philosophy*, pp. 11-15.

[6] *Ibid*, pp. 28-29.

[7] *Ibid*, pp. 32-36.

[8] *Ibid*, pp. 36-39.

[9] *Ibid*, pp. 39-42.

Chapter 10

Power's Contributions to Medicine and Science

In the middle of the seventeenth century, there were many physicians in London and several in Oxford and Cambridge but, elsewhere in the provinces, physicians in medical practice were relatively few. Power was the only practising physician in Halifax, although there were several apothecaries and surgeons.

Clinical Medicine

Power's medicine was conventional and based on an extensive education in medicine and science in Cambridge, supplemented by wide reading in a substantial personal library. Power was not innovative in recognising new diseases or devising new treatments, possibly because his creative energy was mainly directed into scientific research. What he did bring to his practice was that it was based on modern anatomy and physiology and especially the discovery of the circulation of the blood. Power was a practitioner of modern medicine, which aimed to identify and treat specific diseases, believing they had different causations. The teachings of Hippocrates and Galen, that diseases were caused by an imbalance of the humours of the body, had no place in his thinking. Consequently, Power did not use bleeding or blistering, nor did he prescribe harsh emetics or purgatives. His main remedies were medicinal herbs, gathered locally or obtained from pharmacists. His medical care could be described as modern but with only occasional use of the chemical remedies, which were being introduced by the Paracelsians. Power's papers refer to only a few clinical cases, which is regrettable, as he was an accurate observer and careful recorder. There are some scattered reports, two of which are described here. One is a case of amaurosis :

> I had the last year a Patient, a young boy of seventeen years old, who fell casually stark blind of his right eye ; in which you could outwardly discover no fault at all (the disease being an *Amaurosis* , or obstruction of the Optic Nerve) for, that nerve being by successful means disobstructed and relaxed, so that the Animal Spirits were able to flow down to the *Retina* again, he shortly after perfectly recovered his sight again, without any relapse at all to this present day.[1]

Power's explanation of his case was that some pressure on the right optic nerve had been relieved. He compared this to his experiments in which the ligation of nerves in dogs caused paralysis and anaesthesia, which states were relieved by relaxing the ligature. He then describes :

... that ordinary example of a mans Leg being asleep (as we call it) for by compression of the Nerves, the propagation of the Spirits into the part is hindered ; for as sense and motion is restored, you may feel something creep into the Leg tingling and stinging ... which is the return of the Animal Spirits into that part again.

The phrase Animal Spirits was in vogue to describe any action of the brain and nervous system and was much in use by the Oxford physician Thomas Willis.

Anatomy and Physiology

Both in anatomy and physiology, Power is an important figure from his confirmation and championing of the discoveries of others. He was thrilled by the work of the circulation of the blood by Harvey, whose observations and experiments he repeated. Another mentor was Glisson, his professor at Cambridge, whose description of the liver and the lymphatic system was another area of anatomy studied by Power. Power made an experimental study of the lymphatic system, influenced by the work of Jean Pecquet (1622-1674), one edition being published in 1651.[2] [3] These researches of Power can be examined in his extensive manuscript collections in the British Library. Those describing the circulation of the blood (1652), the lymphatic system (1654) and chemical physiology (1657) form an impressive body of work, which was never published. It was gathered together for publication under the following title :

Historia Physio-Anatomica Cum Analogia Physio-Chemica

	{	*Chyli*
De motu	{	*Sanguinis*
	{	*Liquoris Nervosi*
	{	*Aquae Lymphaeductum*

Drawn up for the satisfaction of the Ld DelaMere
A.D. 1666
By Henry Power M.D.[4]

It is regrettable that due to Power's ill health and then to his death in 1668, this work was never published. Had it appeared, this book would have added materially to his fame.

Power made an especial study of the eye and was familiar with its detailed anatomy. Using specimens from his butcher, he wrote :

Take a fresh eye, and, in a frosty Evening, place it with the pupil upwards, where it may be frozen through, then in the morning you may cut it as you please. If you cut it with a plain Parallel to the Optick Axis (which section Des-Cartes thought impossible) then shall you see all the Parts, as he has pictured them *pag.* 92. and each part will be very different in colour, and remain in their natural Site, which may be pricked forth in an oyled Paper: By this trick also you shall find, that there is a double Crystalline humour, one circum-included within the other ; if you do but thaw the Crystalline you shall see the outward will pull off from the inward ...

Then follows instructions for mounting parts of the eye on the stage of his microscope for more detailed scrutiny. Power's descriptions amplified those of Kepler, Descartes, Scheiner, and Hugenius, which sometimes he corrected. In his examinations of the eye, he acknowledged the assistance of : 'our famous and never to be forgotten Country-man, Master Gascoign of *Middleton*, near *Leeds*, who was unfortunately slain in the Royal Service for his late Majesty ...' Gascoign had decribed the dissection of eyes and had sent specimens and descriptions to Power. The comparative anatomy of the eye he studied in the flea, bee, several species of fly, the butterfly, wood louse and several other invertebrates. No species has only one eye, most have two, but spiders may have four, six or eight.[5] These compound multi-faceted eyes were of great interest, which he conjectured were required when the head of, *e.g.* a spider, could not be easily turned.

In verifying the observations of Harvey, the heart and major blood vessels were examined in dogs. The study of the two-chambered heart in many species of invetebrates has been described in chapter 9. Power had no access to cadavers for human dissection and subsequent to his medical studies at Cambridge had no opportunity to study human anatomy.

Astronomy

Power, owning an early telescope (or telescopes), made many observations of the solar system but was an enthusiastic amateur rather than a dedicated astronomer. He observed planets and their moons, a partial eclipse of the sun by Venus, the track of a comet and the motion of the sun as discerned by sun spots.

Microscopy

Power was an early microscopist, making abundant observations of animal and plant specimens. He used his compound microscope to good effect but at low powers of magnification. Many of his subjects could have been seen with a simple microscope, such as a powerful hand lens. His observations are those of an enthusiastic amateur in natural history, but some of his descriptions are original. Whilst his was the first book published on microscopy in England, the *Centuria observationum microscopicarum* of Pierre Borel (1620-1671) was in

Power's library and had a considerable influence in his research. Hooke's book, being well illustrated, made a more lasting impression on the scientific community but the text is not more informative.[6]

Chemistry

Power shared the current interest in inorganic chemistry, the study of which was then expanding. A major body of his experiments concerned extracts of plants. He studied their colours, which could be changed by adding solutions of acid or alkali, then little understood. These colour changes had interested Robert Boyle, who in 1664 had published his book on colours.[7] In the same year appeared Power's observations on colours, being the first to describe the rainbow and light passing through a prism. Then came his '… several Experiments in the Extraction, Commixtion, and Transcolouration of Tinctures.' :

> First therefore, If into an Infusion of Violets you put some few drops of the oyl of Tartar *per Deliquium*, it will presently strike it into a green Tincture : now if instead of that oyl you put in oyl of Vitriol, it strikes it into a purple Colour : to which if you super-add some drops of Spirit of Harts-Horn, it strikes it green again.
>
> Secondly, If into the Tincture of dried Roses (drawn in Hot-water with oyl of Vitriol after the usual manner) you drop a few drops of Spirit of Harts-Horn, or of Urine, or of oyl of Tartar *per Deliquium*, it will presently strike the red into a green colour ; which by a super-addition of the oyl of Vitriol, you may re-tincture as before.
>
> Thirdly, If into an Infusion of Copperose you shave a little Gall, it presently puts on a Sable inky Colour ; into which if you put a few drops of the Spirit or oyl of Vitriol, it strikes out the Colour immediately, and the water becomes white again ; to which if you super-add a few drops of oyl of Tartar *per Deliquium*, it re-denigrates it again.
>
> Thus a Glass of the Sweet-Spaw-water also, upon the Infusion of Gall, turns into a Claret-colour : but if you drop but a little of the said oyl or spirit into it, it presently eats out the Colour, and the water returns to its primitive clearness again.

Finally Power describes a tincture of Brazil wood, which changes with vinegar, oil of Tartar and oil of Vitriol. These colour changes were known outside scientific circles. On the London stage, an entertainer, named Floram Marchand, after drinking a large amount of tincture of Brazil wood and much water, could vomit into three glasses which contained invisible traces of vinegar, oil of tartar, and oil of Vitriol. Apparently magically, his fluid vomit was in three different colours.

Barometric Pressure

Power was an early experimenter in England of the mercury column, the Torricellian vacuum above the mercury, the measurement of barometric pressure, and its variation with altitude, all of which findings were not new. In chapter 5, we made the case that Power, with his friend Richard Towneley, made the discovery of the constant relationship between the pressure of air and its volume. The procedure of introducing air into the vacuum space and then measuring the height of the mercury columns at the top and foot of a hill was a cumbersome experiment but, being communicated to Boyle, had an important sequel. Boyle, using an air pump, made many more measurements with greater ease, and these established the relationship known as Boyle's Law.[8]

Power's Philosophy

It is inconceivable that Power, in 17th century Halifax, would not be a devout Christian. He came from several generations of clerics occupying Anglican churches in West Yorkshire. But his churchgoing did not seriously impair his acceptance of the facts and discoveries of modern science. As he wrote :

> This is the Age wherin (me-thinks) Philosophy comes in with a Spring-tide; and the Peripateticks may as well hope to stop the current of the Tide, or (with *Xerxes*) to fetter the Ocean, as hinder the overflowing of free Phiosophy : Me-thinks, I see how all the old Rubbish must be thrown away, and the rotten Buildings be overthrown, and carried away with so powerful an Inundation. These are the days that must lay a new Foundation of a more magnificent Philosophy, never to be overthrown : that will Empirically and Sensibily canvas the *Phænomena* of nature, deducing the Causes of things from such originals in Nature, as we observe are reproducible by Art, and the infallible demonstration of Mechanics : and certainly this is the way, and no other, to build a true and permanent Philosophy... [9]

Power never considered that science challenged the overall direction of nature by an all-powerful and all-seeing God. He wrote :

> For Nature itself is nothing else but the Art of God. Then certainly, to find the various turnings, and mysterious process of this divine Art, in the management of this great Machine of the World, must needs be the proper Office of onely the Experimental and Mechanical Philosopher.[10]

For Power, solving scientific problems meant discovering how God had made the intricacies of the world. But the observations and thoughts of other scientists often struggled to conform to the beliefs of the church, and this frequently required adherence to the teachings of Aristotle. Power was greatly influenced by Descartes, which reliance caused difficulties in credulity. Descartes (and Power) did not believe in the existence of a vacuum and consequently the nature of the space above the mercury column required an alternative explanation. It might contain a mystical substance called aether or traces of air or mercury. Either of these explanations was unsatisfactory and Boyle, also facing this puzzle, could not decide which might be the explanation. Descartes also maintained that absence of motion was impossible: no body could be completely at rest.

Power believed in the principle of preformation. A seed contained in miniature all the structures of the complete plant, as he wrote to Thomas Browne :

> ... seeds doe not only potentially containe the formes of their owne specifick plants, but are indeed *plantarum suarum foetus* and as it were a young & embrion'd plant, capsulated & stadled up in severall filmes, huskes & shells.

Similarly the tiny dot in the yolk of a hen's egg might contain '... all the parts of the chick exactly delineated before incubation ...'. Microscopes with greater resolution challenged the theory of preformation, but alternative explanations had to await 300 years till the recognition of DNA which, in the nucleus of every cell, has the required programming.

All scientists stand on the shoulders of their predecessors. Of the many founders of modern science, one was Henry Power of Halifax.

NOTES AND REFERENCES

[1] *Experimental Philosophy,* p. 68.

[2] Power, H. *Inventio Aselliana de Venis Lacteis et du motu chyli* , BL. *Sloane, MS 1343, ff. 41-56.*

[3] Pecquet, J. *(Ioannis Pecqueti) Experimenta nova anatomica.* 1661 (several editions).

[4] British Library. *Sloane. MS. 496, ff. 2-22,* and *ff1393. Ff. 20-50.* A complete copy of this work was sent on 31st August, 1666 to George Booth, 1st Lord Delamere of Dunham Massey, Cheshire. This copy is now amongst the manuscripts of the present Lord Delamere at the Sheffield University Library. It is placed at the end of the Hartlib papers, bundle LXXII.

[5] Power did not encounter spiders with two eyes.

6   Hooke, R. *Micrographia, or, Some physiological descriptions of minute bodies made by magnifying glasses*, 1665. This was published in April 1665, a year and a half after that of Power.

7   Boyle, R. *Experiments and considerations touching Colours*, London, 1664.

8   Boyle, R. *New Experiments Physico-Mechanical*, 2nd edition, Oxford, 1662. It was this second edition that established the data for Boyle's Law.

9   *Experimental Philosophy. p. 192.*

10 *Ibid*, pp. 192-193.

Select Bibliography

Abbreviations

BL   British Library

JHMAS   *Journal of the History of Medicine and Allied Sciences.*
In 1957, 300 years after Harvey's death, 'The William
Harvey Issue' grouped articles in volume 12 of *JHMAS.*

THAS   *Transactions of the Halifax Antiquarian Society*

MANUSCRIPT PRIMARY SOURCES

Beeckman, I. *MD thesis, University of Caen.* An incomplete copy survives in the British Library, BL. 1179. D.9 (3)

British Library, Memorandum Books, 7 vols. Sloane MSS. 1351, 1353-1358.

British Library, *Circulatio sanguinis Inventio Harviena*, Sloane MS 1343.

Sheffield University Library, *Hartlib papers, Bundle VII, no. 29.* The letter from Sir Charles Cavendish to William Petty is reproduced in Webster, 1965, p. 456.

Nottinghamshire Archives, Register of baptisms for Annesley, 1624-1633, PR 2826.

PUBLISHED PRIMARY SOURCES

Browne, Sir T. The correspondence between Power and Browne has been published by G. Keynes, *The Works of Sir Thomas Browne*, vols, 1-6, (London, Faber and Gwyer, becoming Faber and Faber, 1928-1931), 6, pp. 275-295.

Fabricius. *De venarum ostiolis*, (1603), edited by K.J. Franklin, Springfield, Illinois, 1933.

Galen. His description of the cardiovascular system in *On Anatomical Procedures Book VII* and in *De Usum Partium* was translated by C. Singer (London, Wellcome Foundation, 1956), pp. 172-200.

Pascal, B. *Oeuvres de Blaise Pascal*, ed. L. Brunschvicg and P. Boutroux, (Paris, 1908), 2, pp. 365-373.

Pecquet, J. *Experimenta nova anatomica* (Paris, 1651)

Power, H. *Experimental Philosophy in Three Books: Containing New Experiments, Microscopical, Mercurial, Magnetical*, (1663). [Power's copy in the British Library is dated 1663 in his handwriting.] This book reproduces many of Power's manuscripts.

Power, H. His will is reproduced in Clay, J.W., 'Dr Henry Power of New Hall, F.R.S.', *THAS*, 1917, pp. 1-31.

Servetus. Three copies of his *Restitutio Christianismi* survive, in Vienna, Paris, and Edinburgh.

Sinclari, G. *Ars Nova et Magna Gravitas et Levitas*, (Roterodami, 1669), *Dialogus Primus*, pp. 125-149.

OTHER SOURCES

Barwick, J. *Querela Cantabrigensis*, (Oxford, 1646), pp. 10-11.

Beeckman, I. *Journal tenu par lui de 1604-1634*, publié avec une introduction et des notes par Cornelius de Waard. 4 Vols. (Le Haye, 1939-1953). The quotation is from vol.1, p. 36.

Birch, T. *History of the Royal Society of London*, 4 vols. (London, 1756-1757), 1, p. 8 and p. 22.

Bonser, W. 'General Medical Practice in Anglo-Saxon England', In *Science, Medicine, and History*, two volumes, edited by E.A. Underwood (London, Oxford University Press, 1953) 1, pp. 154-163.

Byleby, J.J. 'Boyle and Harvey on the Valves in the Veins', *Bulletin of the History of Medicine*, 1982, 56, pp. 351-367.

Chauvois, L., Two editions, translated into French, *Vie de William Harvey* (Paris, Editions Sedes, 1957), and into English, *The Life of William Harvey* (London, Hutchinson, 1957).

Clay, J.W. 'Dr Henry Power of New Hall, F.R.S.', *THAS*, (Halifax, 1917)

Cohen, H. 'The Germ of an idea or what put Harvey on the scent', *JHMAS, pp. 102-105.*

Cole, F.J. 'Henry Power on the Circulation of the Blood', *JHMAS*, pp. 291-324.

Cole, F.J. 'Harvey's Animals', *JHMAS*, pp. 106-113.

Cox, T. *A Popular History of the Grammar School of Queen Elizabeth at Heath, Halifax* (Halifax, 1879).

Debus, A.G. *The English Paracelsians* (New York, 1966).

Ferrario, E.V. 'William Harvey's Debate with Caspar Hofmann on the Circulation of the Blood', *JHMAS*, 1960, 15, pp. 7-21.

Franklin, K.L. *Movement of the Heart and Blood in Animals*, by William Harvey, translated from the Latin (Oxford, Blackwell Scientific Publications, 1957).

Franklin, K.L. 'On translating Harvey', *JHMAS*, pp. 114-119.

Galileo, G. *Le Opera*, (Florence, 1894), IV, p.167.

Galileo, G. *Dialogues concerning two new sciences*. English translation of the 1638 text by H. Crew and A. de Salvio, (London and New York, 1914). Reprint (New York, 1954).

Gent, T. *The Ancient and Modern History of the Loyal Town of Ripon*, (York, 1673-1778), pp. 13-73.

Giles, C. 'New Hall, Elland; The Story of a Pennine Gentry House from c. 1490 to the mid-19th Century'. In *Old West Riding* (Oldgate, Huddersfield, 1981), ed. G. Redmonds. Vol. 1. No. 2.

Gotfredsen, E. 'The Reception of Harvey's Doctrine in Denmark', *JHMAS*, pp. 202-208.

Guthrie, D. 'The Evolution of Cardiology'. In *Science, Medicine, and History*, 2 volumes, edited by E.A. Underwood, (London, Oxford University Press, 1953), 2, pp. 508-517.

Haddad, S.I. and Khairallah, A.A. 'A forgotten chapter in the history of the circulation of the blood', *Annals of Surgery*, 1936, 104, pp. 1-8.

Hanson, J.W. 'The Mulcture Hall', *THAS*, 1935, 1-19.

Harvey, W. *Exercitatio Anatomica De Motu Cordis un Animalibus*, (Frankfurt, William Fitzeri, 1628).

Hughes, J.T. 'Sir Thomas Browne, Shibden Dale, and the Writing of *Religio Medici*', *Yorkshire History Quarterly*, (Settle, 2000) 5, pp. 89-94.

Hughes, J.T. 'Henry Power (1626-1668) of New Hall, Elland and Experiments on Barometric Pressure', *THAS*, 2002, pp. 14-26.

Hughes, J.T. 'Dr Henry Power (1626-1668) : The Medical Practice of a Halifax Physician', *THAS*, 2003, 11, pp. 56-67.

Hughes, J.T. 'Observations and Experiments of Dr Henry Power (1626-1668) Supporting William Harvey's *De Motu Cordis*', *THAS*, 2005, 13, pp. 34-46.

Keynes, G. *The Life of William Harvey* (Oxford, The Clarendon Press, 1978).

Knowles Middleton, W.E. 'The Place of Torricelli in the History of the Barometer', Isis, (Philadelphia, 1963), 54, pp. 11-28.

Leake, C.D. *Anatomical Studies on the Motion of the Heart and the Blood. A modern English translation of William Harvey's De Motu Cordis* (Springfield, Illinois, USA, Charles C. Thomas, 1928, 1931, & 1941).

Leibowitz, J.O. 'Early accounts of the valves in the veins', *JHMAS*, pp. 189-196.

Macleod, J.J.R. 'Harvey's experiments on circulation', *Annals of Medical History*, 1928, 10, pp. 338-348.

Maignan, E. *Cursus philosophicus concinnatus ex notissimus cuique princips.* (Toulouse, 1653) The four volumes are paged as one, pp. 1925-1936.

Midgely, S. *Halifax and its Gibbet Law placed in a True Light*, printed by J. How for William Bentley (Halifax, 1708).

Nicholson, M. 'The Early Stage of Cartesianism in England', *Studies in Philology* (Chapel Hill, USA, 1929), 26, pp. 356-374.

Osler, W. 'Michael Servetus', *Johns Hopkins Hospital Bulletin*, 1910, 21, pp. 1-11.

O'Malley, C.D. and J.B. de C.M. Saunders. *Leonardo da Vinci's 'On the Human body'*, (New York, Henry Schuman, 1952), pp. 216-217.

O'Malley, C.D. *Michael Servetus (1511?-1553). A translation of his Geographical, Medical, and Astrological Writing*, (Berkeley, Los Angeles, USA, University of California Press, 1953).

O'Malley, C.D. ' A Latin translation of Ibn Nafis (1547) related to the problem of the circulation of the blood', *JHMAS*, pp. 248-253.

O'Malley, C.D. 'Medical Education during the Renaissance'. In *The History of Medical Education*, edited by C.D. O'Malley, (Berkeley, Los Angeles, and London, 1970), pp. 89-102.

Patrides, C.A. *The Cambridge Platonists* (London, 1969 and Cambridge, 1980).

Pawson, G.P.H. *The Cambridge Platonists and their Place in Religious Thought* (London, 1930).

Peile, J. *Christ's College* (London, 1900).

Peile, J. *Biographical Register of Christ's College*, 2 vols, (Cambridge, 1910).

Power, D'Arcy. *William Harvey* (London, T Fisher Unwin, 1897).

Raach, J.H. *A Directory of English Country Physicians* 1603-1643, (London, 1962), pp. 119-128.

Rey, J. *Essays sur recherche de la cause pour laquelle l'estain et la plomb augmentent de poids quand on les calcine.* (Bazas 1630)

Roach, J.R.C. *A History of the County of Cambridge , and the Isle of Ely*, (OUP, 1959)

Rolleston, H.D. 'Harvey's Predecessors and Contemporaries', *Annals of Medical History*, 1928, 10, pp. 323-337.

Rolleston, H.D. *The Cambridge Medical School* (Cambridge, 1932), pp. 151-155.

Rook, A., ed. *Cambridge and its Contribution to Medicine*, (??, 1971)

Sisson, J.L. *Historic Sketch of the Parish Church, Wakefield*, (Wakefield, 1824), pp. 40-41.

Stead, J. 'Dr Henry Power and his alterations at New Hall, Elland'. In *Old West Riding Books*, ed. J. Stead (Huddersfield, 1980), vol. 8, pp. 8-17.

Temkin, O. *Galenism: Rise and Decline of a Medical Philosophy* (Ithaca and London, 1973), p. 103.

Thoresby, R. *Ducatus Leodinensis*, edited by T.D. Whitaker (1816).

Thoroton, R. *The Antiquities of Nottinghamshire* (Nottingham, 1677). The picture of Annesley House faces p. 252.

Throsby, J. *History of Nottinghamshire* (Nottingham, 1790), vol. 2, pp. 266-270.

Venn, J. and J.A. Venn, *Alumni Cantabridgiensis*, (Cambridge, 1924), part 1, vol. 3, p. 389.

Waard, C. de, *L'expérience barometrique, ses antecédents et ses explications. Etude historique.* (Thours, 1936).

Waard, C de, *Correspondence de P. Marin Mersenne, religieux minime*. Vols. 1-17, (Paris, 1936), 2, pp. 282-283.

Walker, R.M. 'Francis Glisson'. In Rook, 1971, pp. 35-47.

Webster, C. 'The Discovery of Boyle's Law and the Concept of the Elasticity of Air in the Seventeenth Century', *Archive for History of Exact Sciences*, (Berlin and New York, 1965), 2, pp. 441-502.

Webster, C. 'Richard Townley (1629-1707), The Townley Group and Seventeenth-Century Science', *Transactions of the Historic Society of Lancashire and Cheshire*, (Liverpool, 1966), 118, pp. 51-76.

Weil, E. 'William Fitzer, the Publisher of Harvey's *De Motu Cordis*, 1628', *The Library*, 24, 1943, pp. 142-164.

Weil, E. 'The Echo of Harvey's *De Motu Cordis* (1628)', *JHMAS*, pp. 167-174. Power appears in 1652.

Whitteridge, G. *An Anatomical Disputation Concerning the Movement of the Heart and Blood in Living Creatures*, by William Harvey, translated from the Latin, (London, Blackwell Scientific Publications, 1976).

Willis, R. *The Works of William Harvey*, (London, Sydenham Society, 1847).

Wood, A.A. *Athenae Oxoniensis & The Fasti*, ed. P. Bliss (London, 1820). The reference to Jonathan Maud of Halifax is given in vol. 4, p. 173.

INDEX